How to Automate Both New & Existing Homes

By: Robert N. Bucceri

© Copyright

ISBN 0-9700057-3-3

© 2004 Silent Servant, Inc.

E-mail: swdbook4@aol.com

Disclaimer

Electricity is very dangerous. Use extreme caution when working on electrical systems. Do not attempt to work on or install electrical components while circuits are hot. Always turn off the appropriate circuit breaker or disconnect switching device before beginning work. Confirm that circuits are turned off by using an electrical meter at each specific work location even when you think the circuit breaker or disconnect is off. A Breaker can be mislabeled or thought to be the proper disconnect.

Electrical drawings and information shown and described in this manual are intended for educational purposes only. Some methods described may not be appropriate for certain applications. All electrical equipment shall be installed per the manufacturer's installation instructions and recommendations. Equipment manufacturers are consistently developing improvements and modifications to electrical components. Wiring requirements may change without notice. Consult the manufacturer's instructions before installing any equipment.

Electrical work should be performed by a Licensed Master Electrician. All installations shall conform to the National Electric Code (N.E.C.) as well as to local Electrical codes, amendments and others.

Users of X10 based systems must be careful when transmitting X10 codes to modules controlling appliances. X10 based systems should not be used for life safety purposes.

If X10 systems are used to turn ON electric heaters or other appliances, fire danger can exist if there is an appliance or control component failure, or if an appliance accidentally lights a flammable material. It is not recommended to control appliances with electrical heating elements using Power-line Carrier protocols unless appliances have their own internal auto shut-off control function.

Silent Servant, Inc. assumes no responsibility for injuries or damage caused by or during the installation of electrical systems or controls.

Always confirm that control methods used will not cause damage to existing equipment, structure as a whole or injury to individuals.

TABLE OF CONTENTS

Chapter One

X10 Power-Line Carrier and Hardwired Home Automation Systems

1-1 Home Automation: Most people who are introduced to home automation for the first time will generally ask two basic questions. What is it and what does it do? Some people even ask how does it work? We will answer these questions by first introducing two different types of Home Automation technologies, and reinforce this by describing and illustrating over 140 Home Automation features that you can incorporate into your system. Whether you are just beginning to learn about home automation or whether you are already up to speed on this technology, we believe you will benefit from the information provided by this book.

Just about everyone can benefit from the wide variety of available home automation features. Once a family has experienced specific features that work well within their lifestyles, they will wonder how they did without them. Just imagine if you had to get up off the couch every time you want to change the channel or raise the volume. Imagine having to get out of your car and manually open the garage door and get back in the car to drive it into the garage before manually closing the door. Before we had the convenience of remote control we performed these functions manually on a daily basis because it was our only means. Once remote control technology became affordable for the purpose of controlling the TV and garage door, it grew to become common place in our society and we now rarely look back.

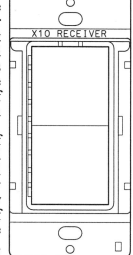

Home Automation provides the family with a similar feel of convenience we experienced the first time we used a handheld remote. All of us will agree that remote control of an electrical device is a great feature. What really gets a person's attention is how home automation takes convenience to a much higher level by incorporating semi-automatic control and fully automatic control of electrical devices using the decision making capability of a Home Controller. Control of a whole series of electrical loads at one time, called a Macro, that is initiated by an individual is what I like to call semi-automatic control. Control of a whole series of electrical loads without interaction or initiation from an individual, is what I like to call fully automatic control. We will discuss this further on page 13.

When the whole family lives with the convenience of remote control, semi-automatic control and fully automatic control of the home's lighting, appliances, air conditioning, pool/spa, ceiling fans, audio/video equipment, arm/disarm security functions, etc, and the wide variety of modes, they will again, rarely look back.

Not only does a home automation system provide convenience, it also provides safety, security, entertainment, energy management and peace of mind.

This book is not highly technical and should not scare you off. This is because it is written in a format that you can easily follow, which allows you to quickly get up to speed on the methods used to automate your place of residence.

As you will find out or already know, home automation is a very interesting subject and in fact can be quite fascinating once you experience some of the features in your own home. The types of home automation system protocols that we will soon cover, do not require that you automate your whole house all at once, if that is your intentions, and you certainly do not need a contractor to install it and set it up.

You can begin developing your home automation system by adding a few features to your place of residence and as the need or desire for addition features arise, you can easily add the supporting equipment.

1-2 X10 Control: One of the home automation protocols that we cover is X10 Power-Line Carrier Technology. X10 is a language that provides a means of communication between a Transmitter and a Receiver switch, which are the two main components used in a home automation system of this kind. An X10 Transmitter sends signals over the power lines from one location in the home, while an X10 Receiver switch located in another location in the home reads these signals and performs specific control functions.

X10 signals consist of short bursts of radio frequency (RF) digital information that travels over the 120V power lines throughout the home. That's right, RF signals are carried over the power wiring and do not travel through the air like they do when using a garage door remote. The main advantage of the X10 protocol is that the installation of wire is not required because they already exist. To control an electrical load remotely, all a user needs to do is add a Receiver switch and a Transmitter to a 120V system. This is performed by simply plugging the electric load into a Receiver switch and then plug in the Receiver switch and Transmitter into wall power receptacles in different locations of the home. Wired-in Receiver switches can also be used to replace existing mechanical wall switches and wired-in Transmitters can be added to the electrical system to initiate control of a load. This will be further explained and illustrated on the following pages.

X10 signals are transmitted over the power lines superimposed and carried by the AC sine wave at a frequency of 120 kHz. Electrical noise and interference generated from electrical equipment such as computers, TVs, fluorescent lights and others normally exist near the positive and negative peaks of the 60 Hz sine wave as shown in Figure 1-1. This is why X10 signals are designed to travel along the zero degree crossing of the sine wave in an effort to avoid electrical noise and X10 signal disruption. This process of transporting X10 communications is illustrated in Figure 1-2.

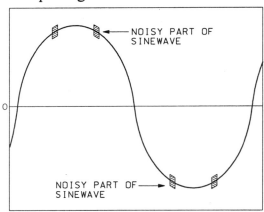

FIGURE 1-1   SHOWS NOISY PART OF SINEWAVE

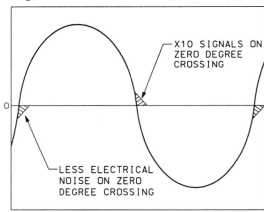

FIGURE 1-2   X10 SIGNAL PATH ON SINEWAVE

X10 signals sent by a Transmitter are carried over the power lines for one or more Receiver switches to accept before performing the desired control functions. Transmitters do not directly switch electrical loads ON and OFF or perform dimming and brightening functions. They transmit the desired control commands and are not wired to an electrical load such as the Living Room lights. The Receiver switch; however, is wired to the electrical load and performs the switching and dimming functions only after receiving the proper series of digital X10 codes sent by a Transmitter.

There can be just a few Receiver switches or more than 50 Receiver switches installed in a home to automate lighting, ceiling fans, garage doors, property access gate, security system, heating and cooling system, window coverings and so on. There can be a few Transmitters or more than 10 Transmitters in a whole house automation system. Since there is more than one Receiver switch and Transmitter in a home automation system, how does each Receiver switch know whether a Transmitter is talking to it specifically or not? A Receiver switch will know when it should respond because it will be assigned a specific address that is the same code assigned to the Transmitter that sends the signals.

Receivers will generally have two 16 position rotary dials used to select address codes. There are also Receiver switches that have their addresses assigned by performing a electronic sequence. To keep this simple; however, the two 16 position rotary dials enable each Receiver switch to be set to one of 256 possible addresses used for identification purposes between Transmitters and Receivers. One address dial consists of **Letter** codes **A** through **P**. The other dial consists of **Number** codes **1** through **16**. Some examples of addresses may include: **A1, B4, E16, J7, N2**, etc. For a Receiver switch to respond to a Transmitters request, all one needs to do is take a small screwdriver and turn the dials to provide an **A1** address, for instance, and then adjust the dials on the Transmitter to **A1** also. Refer to page 4 and follow steps 1, 2 & 3 to see how this is performed. When the corresponding Transmitter button is pressed by the user to turn ON the Living Room lamp, for instance, all the Receiver switches in the system will hear the series of transmission codes over the power lines but only the Receivers switches set to the correct address will respond. To be more specific, the following sequence of codes must take place and be heard before a Receiver switch will respond. If you have difficulty following the next paragraph, it will not be a problem because you really don't need to understand the different types of codes and how they work to be able to automate your home. We will, however, provide this information for those of you that really wants to get into the nuts and bolts of the inner workings.

All Receivers switches in the home monitor the power lines for a **start** code. The **start** code is a binary code equal to 1110. A Receiver switch will need to receive this binary 1110 code for two full sine waves before it begins monitoring the power lines for an **address** code. If the **letter** code of the Receiver switch matches the **letter** code on the power lines, the Receiver switch will then compare the next 5 bits of information, which represents the **number** code. When the **letter** code and the **number** code match what is seen on the power lines, the Receiver switch will monitor the lines for a **function** code. For reliable operation, Transmitters send this series of **letter** codes and **number** codes twice. A delay of three cycles of the sine wave exists between the identification series of commands and the command series of codes transmitted. The function or command portion of the transmission also begins with a **start** code. The Receiver switch again compares the **letter** code and if this comparison is satisfied and the next 5 bits equal an OFF command, the Receiver switch will turn OFF. If a Receiver switch **letter** code matches but the **number** code does not, the Receiver switch will continue monitoring the power lines for a possible 'All Receivers **OFF**' command. A possible 'All Receivers **ON**' command is also monitored for when specific Receivers switches provide this capability. This is the method used to communicate from a Transmitter to a Receiver.

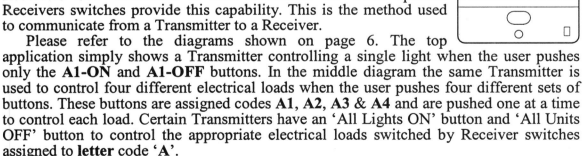

Please refer to the diagrams shown on page 6. The top application simply shows a Transmitter controlling a single light when the user pushes only the **A1-ON** and **A1-OFF** buttons. In the middle diagram the same Transmitter is used to control four different electrical loads when the user pushes four different sets of buttons. These buttons are assigned codes **A1, A2, A3 & A4** and are pushed one at a time to control each load. Certain Transmitters have an 'All Lights ON' button and 'All Units OFF' button to control the appropriate electrical loads switched by Receiver switches assigned to **letter** code 'A'.

The bottom diagram illustrates the use of a Home Controller along with a wall Transmitter. The Home Controller is programmed, so **IF** it receives **A1-ON** signals from the Transmitter, it will turn around and transmit virtually any number of different pre-programmed automated home control responses. Responses can consist of X10 transmissions, I/O Relay Outputs, IR signals to control A/V equipment, voice responses, and ASCII communications to control other system devices.

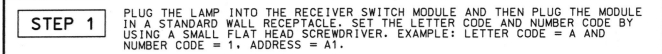

STEP 1 — PLUG THE LAMP INTO THE RECEIVER SWITCH MODULE AND THEN PLUG THE MODULE IN A STANDARD WALL RECEPTACLE. SET THE LETTER CODE AND NUMBER CODE BY USING A SMALL FLAT HEAD SCREWDRIVER. EXAMPLE: LETTER CODE = A AND NUMBER CODE = 1, ADDRESS = A1.

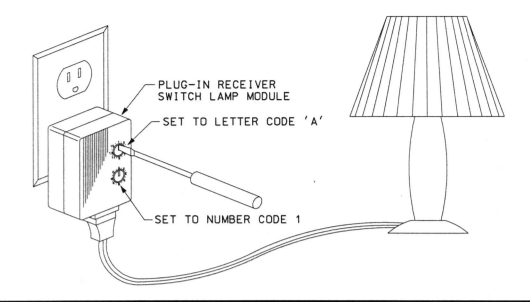

PLUG-IN RECEIVER
SWITCH LAMP MODULE

SET TO LETTER CODE 'A'

SET TO NUMBER CODE 1

STEP 2 — PLUG THE TABLE TOP TRANSMITTER INTO ANY STANDARD WALL RECEPTACLE. SET THE LETTER CODE USING A SMALL FLAT HEAD SCREWDRIVER AND SET THE NUMBER CODE USING THE SLIDE SWITCH. SET TRANSMITTER TO THE SAME CODE AS THE THE RECEIVER SWITCH MODULE SHOWN ABOVE.

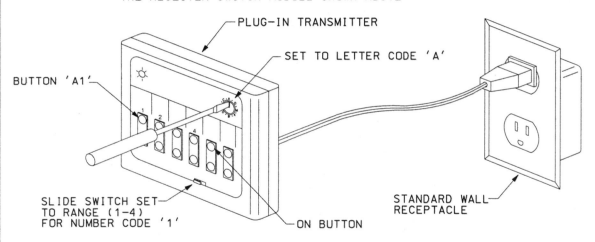

PLUG-IN TRANSMITTER

SET TO LETTER CODE 'A'

BUTTON 'A1'

SLIDE SWITCH SET
TO RANGE (1-4)
FOR NUMBER CODE '1'

ON BUTTON

STANDARD WALL
RECEPTACLE

STEP 3 — TO OPERATE, PUSH TRANSMITTER BUTTON 'A1' AND THE 'ON' BUTTON TO TURN THE LAMP ON. THEN PUSH THE DIM BUTTON TO DIM THE LAMP TO THE DESIRED BRIGHTNESS LEVEL. PUSH BRIGHT BUTTON TO BRIGHTEN THE LIGHT.

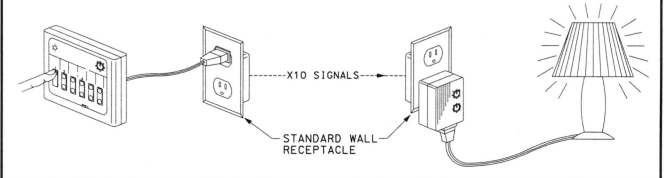

X10 SIGNALS

STANDARD WALL
RECEPTACLE

DIFFERENT TYPES OF RECEIVER SWITCHES

APPLIANCE MODULE APPLICATION

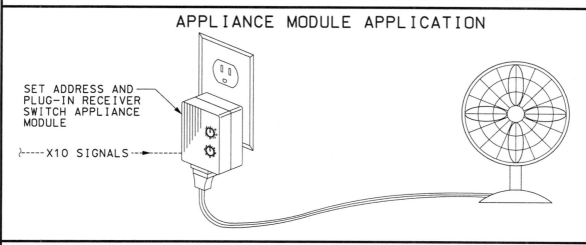

SET ADDRESS AND PLUG-IN RECEIVER SWITCH APPLIANCE MODULE

}----X10 SIGNALS---->

WIRED-IN INCANDESCENT LIGHT RECEIVER SWITCH APPLICATION

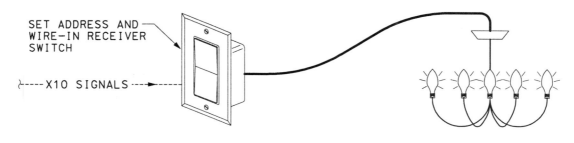

SET ADDRESS AND WIRE-IN RECEIVER SWITCH

}----X10 SIGNALS--->

WIRED-IN APPLIANCE RECEIVER SWITCH APPLICATION

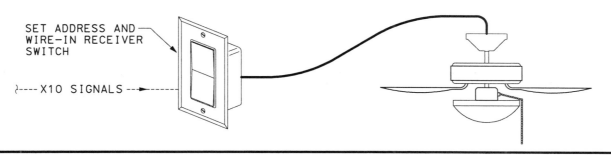

SET ADDRESS AND WIRE-IN RECEIVER SWITCH

}----X10 SIGNALS--->

WIRED-IN RECEPTACLE APPLIANCE RECEIVER SWITCH APPLICATION

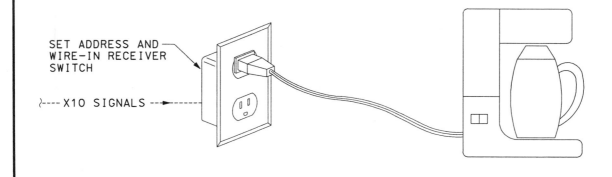

SET ADDRESS AND WIRE-IN RECEIVER SWITCH

}----X10 SIGNALS---->

WIRED-IN TRANSMITTER AND RECEIVER SWITCH APPLICATION
PUSH A1-ON OR A1-OFF BUTTONS TO CONTROL THIS SINGLE LIGHT

BUTTON A1-ON
BUTTON A1-OFF

DIRECT TRANSMISSION

X10 SIGNALS
A1-ON

CODE = A1

ADDRESS = A1

WIRED-IN TRANSMITTER AND RECEIVER SWITCHES APPLICATION
PUSH INDIVIDUAL BUTTONS TO CONTROL INDIVIDUAL ELECTRICAL LOADS

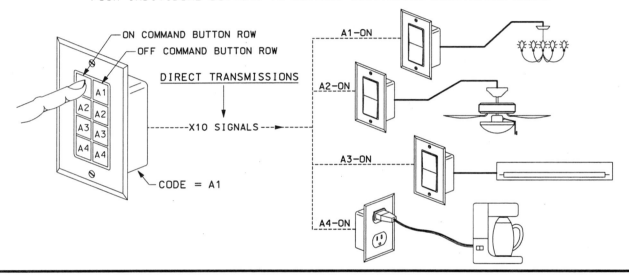

ON COMMAND BUTTON ROW
OFF COMMAND BUTTON ROW

DIRECT TRANSMISSIONS

X10 SIGNALS

CODE = A1

A1-ON

A2-ON

A3-ON

A4-ON

USING TRANSMITTER AND HOME CONTROLLER APPLICATION
IF THE HOME CONTROLLER RECEIVES A1-ON SIGNALS, IT WILL TRANSMIT C4-ON, E7-OFF, H2-ON & J9-OFF SERIES OF SIGNALS, WHICH IS CALLED A MACRO

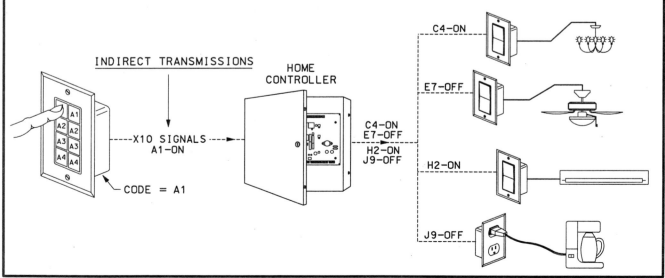

INDIRECT TRANSMISSIONS

HOME CONTROLLER

X10 SIGNALS
A1-ON

CODE = A1

C4-ON
E7-OFF
H2-ON
J9-OFF

C4-ON

E7-OFF

H2-ON

J9-OFF

Home Controller Hardwired (I/O) Input/Output Option

1-3 Hardwired I/O Option: As we had mentioned earlier, the X10 Power-line Carrier protocol does not require the addition of control wiring to automate your new or existing home. When you are building a new home and have the opportunity to pull control wiring through the home before the drywall goes up, then you can take advantage of incorporating hardwired control to work along with the X10 control subsystem.

When a home is properly tested for 'X10 signal strength' and 'electrical noise' prior to the system installation and the appropriate steps are taken to allow the system to work properly, an X10 system can be a dependable means of controlling almost all of the electrical loads in a home.

There are a few electrical loads that should be controlled by hardwired means because Power-line Carrier Control Systems can at times experience signal collision and changes in the level of electrical noise on the power lines that can disrupt communications. These factors can cause Receiver switch response problems or the premature activation of electrical loads on rare occasions. For this reason, there are some electrical loads that can benefit from an increase in control reliability. By utilizing the hardwired option to control loads considered to be most critical in conjunction with a Power-line Carrier sub-system used to control less critical loads, the overall home automation system will become a well rounded means of dependably controlling all electrical loads on the property.

The I/O option is used to establish hardwired connections and control of certain types of electrical loads. Some electrical loads that are generally controlled using the hardwired I/O option include: CCTV surveillance cameras, garage doors, property access gate, vehicle detection system, security system (arm/disarm functions) and the activation of the 'Arriving Home Mode'.

The I/O of the Home Controller is hardwired to receive Digital Inputs and Analog Inputs from sensory components to base control decisions on. After receiving the proper input, the Home Controller will respond by initiating I/O Relay Outputs, Transmit X10 or IR signals or send ASCII communications to perform the intended control functions.

Two of the Home Controllers with hardwired Input and Output capabilities that are illustrated in this book include the *Stargate* and *CommStar*. These are powerful home automation controllers that centralize control of lighting, appliances, security system, heating and cooling system, home theater, audio/video systems, pool/spa, irrigation systems, etc. while maintaining the ability to control these systems manually.

A Home Controller is used to provide the homeowner with a system that offers decision making capability. One of the primary purposes of a Home Controller is to perform modes of operation. A 'mode' can consist of functions that control one or more electrical loads. In the Leaving Home Mode, for instance, after an occupant pushes a Transmitter button on the way out the door, the Home Controller sends out a long series of commands called a Macro. The Macro turns off the lights, ceiling fans, water heater, arms the security system, closes the drapes, turns off all A/V equipment, etc. The Home Controller knows what to control and when to control it when it receives the correct input. Inputs can range from the correct date and/or time of day, at sunset or sunrise, or when programming Flags are Set or Clear as well as other conditions.

7

Home Controller INPUT Types: Use in Event **IF** statement. See page 13

- **X10 command signals** transmitted over the power lines and received by the Home Controller.
- **IR signals** sent by an IR Transmitter and received by the Home Controller.
- **Digital Input** received by the Home Controller.
- **Analog Input** received by the Home Controller.
- **RS-232 communications** received by the Home Controller from other control devices.
- **RS-485 ASCII communications** received by the Home Controller from other types of control devices such as the *RCS* TR15 Thermostat and LCD or LED keypads.

Once the Home Controller receives the correct **Input**, it will know to perform the correct **Outputs** to control one or more electrical devices. These Outputs may include the following:

Home Controller **Output** Types: Use in Event **THEN** statement. See page 13

- **X10 commands signals** sent by the Home Controller to control electrical loads.
- **IR command signals** sent by the Home Controller to control A/V equipment.
- **Relay Outputs** performed by the Home Controller to control, for instance, (garage door, property access gate, pool pump, etc.).
- **RS-232 communications** sent by the Home Controller to other types of controllers.
- **RS-485 ASCII communications** sent by the Home Controller to other types of controllers such as the *RCS* TR15 Thermostat and LCD or LED keypads.

Stargate and *CommStar* Home Controllers both have an I/O (Input/Output) board that provides **8 Analog Inputs**, **16 Digital Inputs** and **8 Relay Outputs** shown below in Figure 1-3.

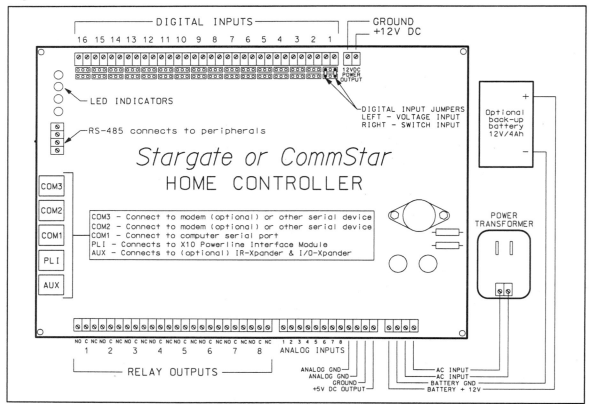

FIGURE 1-3 Stargate or CommStar Home Controller

8

There are two different types of **DIGITAL INPUTS**:

- Switched INPUT
- Voltage INPUT

Switched Input Example:

When a dry contact switch closes, the Home Controller reads that the Digital Input is ON. When the dry contact switch opens, the Home Controller reads that the Digital Input is OFF. Digital Inputs can be initiated with either a dry contact closure from a motion detector or other sensory device. (See glossary page 121 for dry contact definition).

Automatic activation of the **Arriving Home Mode** using a switched Digital Input is described as follows: When an occupant approaches the home in a vehicle or on foot, they will use a secure RF handheld remote that closes dry contacts within an RF receiver. These contacts are wired to a pair of Digital Input terminals that close a circuit and cause the Digital Input to GO-ON. The Home Controller will detect this condition and securely initiate the **Arriving Home Mode.**

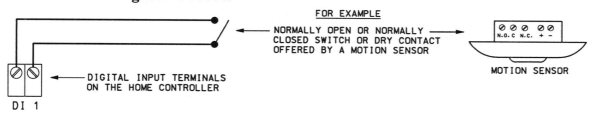

FOR EXAMPLE

NORMALLY OPEN OR NORMALLY CLOSED SWITCH OR DRY CONTACT OFFERED BY A MOTION SENSOR

DIGITAL INPUT TERMINALS ON THE HOME CONTROLLER

DI 1

N.O. C N.C. + −

MOTION SENSOR

Voltage Input Example:

A voltage Input can switch a 4 - 24V DC differential across Digital Input terminals. When the doorbell rings a low voltage is present. In this case the Home Controller reads that the Digital Input is ON. When this occurs the Home Controller will know to transmit X10 signal over the power lines to activate a chime located in the backyard. When the doorbell stops ringing the Home Controller reads that the Digital Input is OFF.

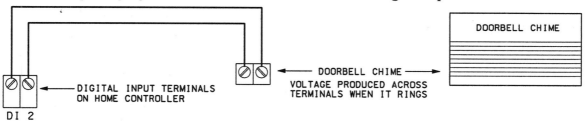

DOORBELL CHIME

DIGITAL INPUT TERMINALS ON HOME CONTROLLER

DI 2

DOORBELL CHIME

VOLTAGE PRODUCED ACROSS TERMINALS WHEN IT RINGS

Analog Input Example:

Analog Inputs are connected to an Analog to Digital Converter that convert analog voltages into a digital representation compatible with *Stargate* and *CommStar*. When either of these Home Controllers read an Analog Input, it reads a value in the range of (0-255), which represents a voltage from 0-5V applied to an input. The table shown below shows some typical input voltages and what Stargate and CommStar read.

Input Voltage	*Stargate/CommStar Reads*
0 volts	0
1 volt	51
2.5 volts	128
4 volts	205
5 volts	255

In the Analog Input example shown below, a temperature sensor is connected to an Analog Input. As the temperature increases over time, the Analog Input voltage will increase linearly. When the temperature rises to the equivalent value of 100°F; for instance, a decision by the Home Controller will position draperies closed to help reduce the rate of heat gained by the home.

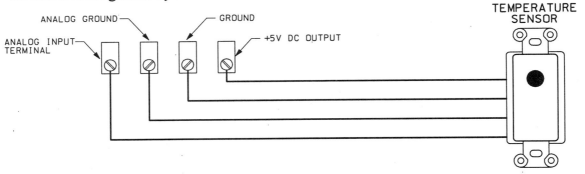

Relay Output Momentary Closure Example:

A Relay Output ON command from the Home Controller consists of a low voltage switch closure that occurs inside the Home Controller. In the example shown below, a low voltage switch inside the Home Controller momentarily closes to open the garage door. Another momentary closure will close the garage door.

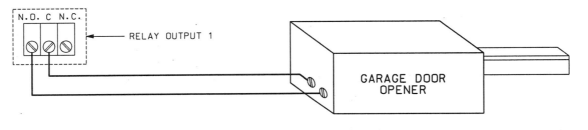

Relay Output Maintained Closure Example:

In this Relay Output example, the Relay Output closes (Relay ON), which closes a low voltage circuit that energizes a starter coil to close the starter contacts that in turn start the pool pump. The Relay Output remains closed to maintain the starter contacts closed in order to run the pump. When the Relay Output opens, the starter coil will become de-energized and the pump will stop.

I/O Relay Outputs are rated for 500ma @ 28V AC/DC and are used to open and close low voltage control circuits. These control circuits can be used to start and stop motors, control air conditioning equipment, turn water heaters ON & OFF and open or close the drapes to mention a few.

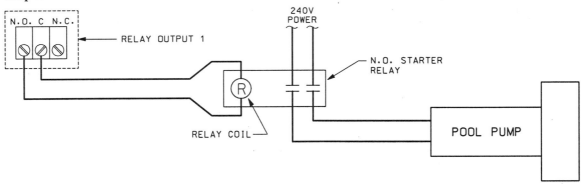

1-4 Controlling the System by Phone: Accessing control of single electrical loads or modes using a touch-tone phone is a powerful and convenient means of initiating home automation features. Touch-tone phones are convenient controllers especially cordless phones since they can be carried to function as a mobile controller anywhere on the property. In fact touch-tone phones can be used to access control of electrical devices in the home from anywhere in the world. This is performed by first calling the home. After the Telephone Controller answers the phone, it prompts the caller to enter a 4-digit security access code that allows the caller to access the system to have control of virtually any electrical load on the property. When controlling electrical devices from on the property, all a user needs to do is pick up the phone and enter commands using the phone keypad buttons. Simple telephone touch-tones are recognized by the Telephone Controller and will transmit the correct X10 signals over the power lines to the intended Receiver switches or to the Home Controller. Touch-tones can turn an electrical load ON or OFF as well as Brighten and Dim the lights.

All telephones that produce touch-tone signals can control electrical loads ON and OFF when using a Telephone Controller. Not all touch-tone phones; however, can dim the lights. Only phones that produce a constant tone when holding down a button on the phone keypad can provide dimming commands.

To control a home automation system using a touch-tone phone from any anywhere in the world, a method must be developed to set-up **letter** and **number** address codes. This must be accomplished in such a manner that the user can easily control virtually any electrical load without having to refer to a list that shows what code controls what load. This is why we have developed what is called the 'Zone Coding' method.

The first digit of a '**Zone Code**' is nothing more than a **letter** code assigned to an area or group of rooms that occupy a certain segment of the home. The second digit of a '**Zone Code**' identifies a specific electrical load or programmed Event within the Zone. The 'Zone Coding' process begins by assigning Zones to areas of the house starting with the largest room in the home. This will generally be a room that is normally occupied much of the time by family members during awake hours. This room; for instance, may be the Family Room. The Family Room is assigned to **Zone 1**, which corresponds to the first letter in the alphabet. This means that all Receiver switches in Zone 1 will be set to **letter** code **A**. **Zone 2** Receiver switches will be set to **letter** code **B** and so on. The designer will select rooms in a clockwise direction following the home's perimeter while assigning Zones in sequence. This will help the user to easily remember or figure out what Zone any electrical load is located in for the user to control the load. To control an electrical load by phone, the first key pressed indicates an ON or OFF command, the second key pressed identifies the Zone where the electrical load is located and the third key pressed identifies the specific electrical load the user wants to control.

Now lets talk about setting up **number** codes. When assigning a **number** code to a Receiver switch that activates the most predominately used light in each Zone, **number** code **5** is used. Number **5** is selected because button **5** on the phone keypad corresponds to **L** = Light shown in Figure 1-4. These LETTERS should not be confused with **letter codes** that identify Zones. If there are three separate automated lights within a Zone, the next two lights will be assigned **number** codes **6 & 7**. This series of numbers will allow the user to easily control all lighting and appliances within any Zone in the home.

The ceiling fan Receiver switch in each Zone should be assigned **number** code **3** since **3** corresponds to **F** = Fan on the phone keypad. A room chime should be assigned **number** code **2** because **2** corresponds to **C** = Chime. The drapery positioner uses **number** code **9** since **9** corresponds to **W** = Window as shown on the phone keypad. This same logic can be used to code and identify any type of electrical load that may arise.

FIGURE 1-4 PHONE KEYPAD

1-5 Controlling the System over the Internet: The *Web-Xpander* is a serial (RS-232) to Ethernet module with embedded Web pages that allow monitoring and control of *Stargate* through the Internet and/or local network. From anywhere in the world, the homeowner can adjust the home's HVAC thermostat, check the status of the security system, turn ON/OFF lights or any other control feature built into the home automation system. If the home network incorporates a wireless link, the user can enjoy wireless control from their portable pocket PC, webpad or notebook computer.

The residence must receive some type of *Broadband* Internet service that is 'Always-On'. The users, however, can use Dial-up Internet service from a location away from the home to communicate with the *Web-Xpander* for the purpose of making adjustments to the Home Automation System or to simply check the status of the system.

The *Web-Xpander* mounts directly above *Stargate's* Telephone/IVR 'daughter board. The *Web-Xpander* can be connected to a signal PC using a cross-over cable. The second method is to connect the *Web-Xpander* to a Network Hub, which is connected to one or more PCs. The third method is to connect the *Web-Xpander* to a Cable or DSL Router, which provides Internet access to both the *Web-Xpander* and PCs on the local network.

The RS-232 input port connects to the user's PC Com Port for downloading the schedule to *Stargate*. The RS-232 output port connects to the COM-1 port of *Stargate* using a modular cable. The Ethernet port connects to the user's network Router using a standard Ethernet cable and the power terminals connect to *Stargate's* on-board 12V DC power supply.

The *Web-Xpander* can also provide E-mail support and *Stargate* can be programmed to send E-mail messages in response to any condition. If the user's cell phone or PDA is equipped to receive E-mail messages, the user can be automatically notified when the security system status changes (armed, disarmed, alarm, etc.). It can also let the user receive information about temperature in the home or spa, or even the simple reminder to take out the garbage or to take medication.

With the ASCII pass through feature, the *Web-Xpander* can pass ASCII data strings from its Ethernet port to its RS-232 serial port to *Stargate*. This allows networked systems to communicate to *Stargate* and enable the use of a wide variety of user interface options that include both hardware and software.

The *Web-Xpander* setup software includes a utility that copies the user's *Stargate* database that consists of X10, IR, HVAC, Security, I/O, Flags, and Variables from the user's PC and loads them into the *Web-Xpander's* memory. This allows all the user's *Stargate* system devices to be identified by their defined names (Family Room, Master Bedroom, etc.) without having to retype them.

Another feature allows the user to download *Stargate's* schedule over the Internet. This is made possible by downloading an optional software utility called 'COM/IP' from *JDS* Technologies. This software creates a virtual serial port/modem on the user's PC that when dialed actually makes a connection over the Internet. Once this feature is configured, the user can use the WinEVM 'Dial PC Modem' function to connect to *Stargate* through the *Web-Xpander*. WinEVM communicates through the virtual modem port created by COM/IP and functions as if the user connected to *Stargate* over a modem connection. All features including schedule downloads are possible in this configuration.

The *Web-Xpander* can also be configured to automatically synchronize *Stargate's* internal clock daily to maintain an accurate time setting.

The *Web-Xpander's* built-in web page provides an easy to use, point-and-click user interface, which can be viewed and operated from any browser (Internet Explorer, Netscape, etc). Direct access buttons allow the user to navigate through the control menus to control Lighting, Audio/Video equipment, Security, HVAC, X10, Digital Inputs, Analog Inputs, Relays, Timers, Flags, Variables, ASCII, History, Message Log and Telephone Log. Each menu lists devices by their defined names with buttons that display status and provide control. The 'Lighting' menu, for example, lists the defined X10 lights by name with the ON, OFF or Idle buttons that provide direct control and indicate status

1-6 Programming the Home Controller: The Home Controller is intelligent because it is programmed to make decisions based on conditions. It is capable of providing **IF-THEN** or **IF-THEN-ELSE** with **AND-OR** Event logic. In fact the thought process of a Home Controller is similar to how a human thinks. For instance, refer to the programming **Example A** shown on page 14. **IF** — I am a good boy, **THEN** — I can watch TV. The **IF** statement is the condition and the **THEN** statement is the result only when the **IF** statement is true. Refer to **Example B**. IF someone pushes X10 Transmitter button **A1** and it is received by the Home Controller, **THEN** the Home Controller will turn OFF the lights and a ceiling fan. This is what I referred to earlier as semi-automatic control because a person needs to physically initiate the Event by pushing a button. In **Example C**, we illustrate how the Good Night Mode works. **IF** it is 10:00 PM Sunday – Thursday, **THEN**, arm the security system, turn OFF the water heater, etc. This Event is considered to be fully automatic because no one initiated the Event since it was based only on time. We could have used an X10 Photocell Transmitter that sends X10-ON signals when it senses sunset; however, this is to early to run the mode. The Photocell could be set to transmit **X10-OFF** signals 4 hours after sunset that could be used in the Event's **IF** statement as a condition to activate the Good Night Mode. IF A1-OFF signals are received, **THEN** activate the Mode. This would also be considered fully automatic.

The first step to take when building a Schedule is to create a device database. This database tells the Event Manager what electrical loads can be automated. Devices will later be selected from the database to build all of the Events that make-up the Home Controller's Schedule. Devices are individually selected to build the **IF** statement as well as the **THEN** statement of each Event. Devices to define include X10 devices, Timers, Time Labels, Flags, Digital Inputs, Analog Inputs, Relay Outputs, Variables, IR commands, **IF** Macros and **THEN** Macros. Devices may be added, changed or deleted in the database at any time. When building the **IF** statement portion of an Event, one can select from X10 codes received, IR signals received, I/O Digital or Analog Inputs received, whether a particular **Flag** previously defined is **Set** or **Clear**, whether it is Sunrise or Sunset (Dark or Light) or if it is a specific date and time.

After an Event's **IF** statement is complete, the next step is to build the **THEN** statement. This portion of the Event consists of X10 command signals, IR command signal used to control A/V components, Relay Outputs used to control more critical electrical loads along with Timers and Flags. Once the Events are complete and checked, they can be downloaded by simply clicking on '**File**' and '**download schedule**'. After the download is complete, the PC can be disconnected and powered down.

Timers are count down Timers used in an Event's **THEN** statement for the purpose of initiating another Event containing the Timer condition in it's **IF** statement. (As shown in the Good Night Mode **THEN** statement), Time 8 begins counting down and will expire after 15:00 minutes. This Timer is used to allow their son Billy time to get ready for bed before an Event can potentially run. In the '**TIMER 8**' Event, the **IF** condition states that when Timer 8 expires (15 minutes has past), **THEN** Set the 'Billy Flag'. Flags have two states, **Set** or **Clear**. The state of a Flag is used to conditionally communicate to other Events. In the '**BILLY IS WANDERING**' Event's **IF** statement, it states that **IF** Digital Input 'Child Motion' is ON (Motion is detected in Hallway), **THEN** activate voice response from the Home Controller that states "Billy get in bed".

The following is an example of a Variable used in an Event's **IF** statement. An analog temperature sensor located at the Living Room window provides an Analog Input to the Home Controller. **IF** the temperature is more than 100°F, **THEN** automatically close the drapes to reduce the flow of heat entering the home.

Example A: *Human Thought Process*:

IF: ----------------------------**Condition**
I am a good boy

THEN: ----------------------- **Result, Only when the IF Condition is True**
I can watch TV

Example B: *Home Controller Thought Process: Semi-Automatic Control* – Requires
Initiation by pushing button **A1**

IF:
X10 Transmitter button **A1** is pushed and signals are received by the Home Controller

THEN: The Home Controller sends out X10 signals to perform the following:
Turn ON the Living Room
Turn ON the patio lights
Turn ON the Kitchen light
Turn ON the Ceiling fan

Note: When the **IF** statement is true, the Home Controller performs the **THEN** statement

Fully –Automatic Control – Is automatic because it is based on time of day. It could also be based Sunset, X10 signals receiver from Photocell, Flags or other conditions.

EVENT: **GOOD NIGHT MODE:**	*Mode name*
IF	*if*
Time is 10:00 PM .SMTWT.	*If time is 10:00 PM Sun - Thur*
Then	*then*
(Partition ARM	*Arms security system*
(RELAY: WATER HEATER) OFF	*Turn OFF water heater*
(X: LIGHT LOW-V A-5) ON	*Turn ON Living Rm low voltage lights*
(X: LIGHT LV HAL A-6) OFF	*Turn OFF Living Rm halogen light*
(X: LIGHT HALL C-5) Pre-Set Level 70 %	*Turn Hall lights ON to 70% bright*
(X: (X: LIGHT MS BED D-5) Pre-Set Level 70 %	*Turn Master Bedroom lights ON to 70% bright*
(LIGHT BILLY'S BATH C-6) ON	*Turn ON Billy's Bath light*
(X: LIGHT MS BATH K-1) ON	*Turn ON Master Bath light*
(X: LIGHT BILLY'S RM H-9) ON	*Turn ON Billy's Bedoom lights*
(XCMD: B - All Units OFF)	*Turn OFF all Receivers set to letter code B*
(F: BILLY FLAG) Set *Set the Billy Flag to allow*	*'Billy is Wandering Mode' potentially to run*
(TIME 8) LOAD with 0 : 15 : 00	*After 15 minute, activate Timer 8 functions*
End	*End of Event*

EVENT: **TIMER 8**	*Mode name*
IF	*if*
(T: TIME 8) is Expiring	*If it is 15 minutes after the Good Night Mode*
Then	*then*
(F: BILLY FLAG) Set	*Set the Billy Flag*
End	*End of Event*

EVENT: **BILLY IS WANDERING**	*Mode name*
IF	*if*
(BILLY FLAG) is Set	*If the Billy Flag is Set*
and (DI: CHILD MOTION) is ON	*and Billy is detected in Hallway*
Then	*then*
Voice: "Billy get back to bed"	*Billy is told by Home Controller to get back to bed*
End	*End of Event*

Chapter Two
Home Automation
System Feature Presentation

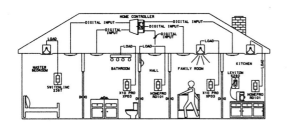

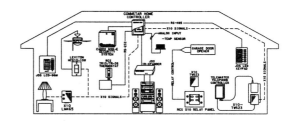

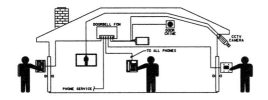

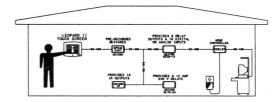

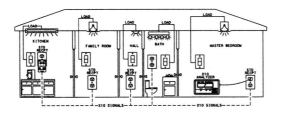

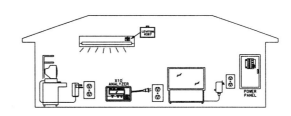

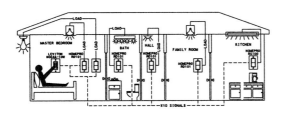

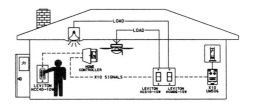

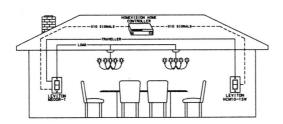

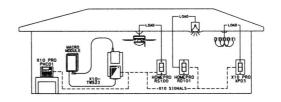

2-1 System Features: The following section of this book is designed to help you easily learn about many of the system features that a typical Home Automation System can provide. It will also explain how each feature works. It goes even one step further by providing either the names of system components or the model numbers of components required to achieve specific home automation functions. This book offers a visual approach to learning about Home Automation Systems along with specific feature information and sequence of operation. This will allow you to better understand what the system components actually go through to achieve the desired end functions.

Over 140 different illustrations and feature descriptions are contained in this book, which is why you will gain a great deal of system design information by the time you have studied each feature. This format will save you many hours of trying to come up with system features that you want to incorporate into your Home Automation System and will also save you time when selecting the proper system components to do the job. You will also enjoy system features from the visual perspective because they are both interesting and uncomplicated.

System components shown in each system feature are not the only type or brand components that can be used to perform the described functions. There are generally a number of different companies that offer virtually the same or similar components that will do the job. Some of these components can be found in the 'Receiver Switch Comparison Chart' on page 119.

Most of the system components represented in this book can be found in the Home Automation System Component Descriptions and Specifications section in Chapter Three. This section will provide you with additional component information such as model number, control characteristics, conductor identifications, voltage (V), amperage (A), volt amp (VA) ratings and physical dimensions. Components that are not found in Chapter Three can be found on the appropriate manufacturer's Web site or on one of the many system component Distributor's Web sites listed on page 120.

The methods illustrated in each system feature are not necessarily the best way or only way to achieve specific Home Automation functions. Most system features can be achieved by using either the X10 approach or the hardwired approach. The X10 approach is generally used exclusively when incorporating home automation into an existing home. A combination of X10 and hardwired control is generally used in systems for new homes. When you plan to use hardwired components in your system it is important to properly plan on where to pull conductors, so you will be able to perform the prep work up front before the drywall goes up.

As you read each feature, it will help to refer back to the appropriate pages for information on X10, Digital and Analog Inputs, Relay Outputs and RS-232 and RS-485 communications. It is also beneficial to take your time and read each sequence of operations and follow the diagrams so you will truly understand how each feature works. Once you see how it is done, you will be able to make-up some of your own features that you would like in your home and know what system components to purchase.

For further information on how to design a Home Automation System, refer to the **Latest Technology in Automated Home Control**. If you would like to incorporate a Structured Wiring System (hardwired approach) into your new home for the purpose of future proofing the home for years to come, refer to the **Structured Wiring Design Manual**. Information on what these books contain is shown at the back of this book.

SYSTEM FEATURE 1
REMOTE CONTROL OF A PLUG-IN LAMP

In this simple control feature, the occupant uses Universal Remote HCCUR to send RF signals to Transceiver TM751. The Transceiver then sends X10 signals over the power lines to be received by plug-in Receiver switch LM465. If the Receiver switch reads the correct X10 codes the lamp will turn ON. The lamp can be dimmed or brightened by holding down the 'volume − and + buttons' respectively on the Universal Remote. ON and OFF commands are initiated by pressing the 'channel + and − buttons' respectively. Refer to page 99 to see the appropriate buttons on the Universal Remote.

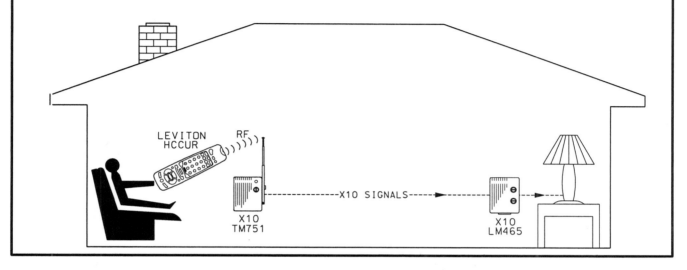

SYSTEM FEATURE 2
AUTOMATED AIR CIRCULATION CONTROL

An occupant pushes the Transmitter button labeled ceiling fan along with the ON button on plug-in tabletop unit 6320. This sends X10 signals over the power lines that are received by Receiver switch HCS10 to turn the ceiling fan ON. If he wants to turn the fan back OFF, he would simple push the OFF button without having to push the fan button first. Control of the ceiling fan speed can generally not be performed without experiencing noise from the fan motor. If the occupant would like to remotely control the floor standing fan, a different button on the Transmitter can be assigned or the same button can be used as long as plug-in Receiver switch AM466 is set to the same X10 address.

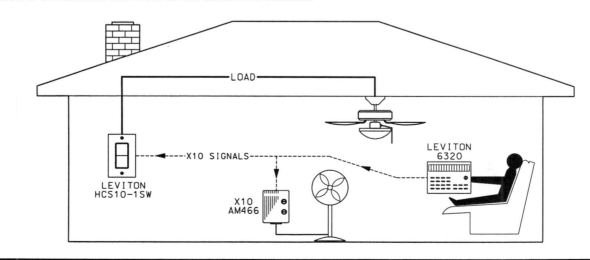

SYSTEM FEATURE 3
SIMPLE METHOD OF AUTOMATING AN APPLIANCE

The coffeepot is plugged into Receiver switch AM466 and the Receiver switch is plugged into a standard power receptacle. The coffee pot is simply automated by using Timer PHT02 that is set to the same X10 code as the Receiver switch. The Timer is set to transmit X10 signals, for instance, at 6:00 each morning to close the Receiver switch and turn ON the coffeepot. The Timer can also be set to turn the coffeepot power OFF, for instance, ½ hour later. The user can also turn OFF the coffeepot by using the Timer keypad located on top of the unit.

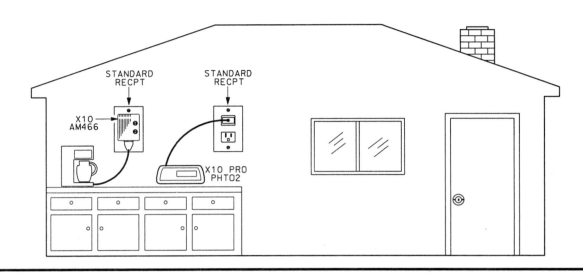

SYSTEM FEATURE 4
A VIRTUAL 3-WAY SWITCH ARRANGEMENT

In a standard residential electrical system, multiple switches in different locations of the home must be wired in conjunction with each other to provide 3-way or 4-way control of an electrical load. When X10 technology became available, 3-way or 4-way switching functions could be achieved without having to wire switches in conjunction with each other. This ability is considered to be one of the most basic but powerful features of X10 technology. This is called the virtual 3-way switch, which is most commonly referred to as remote control. It is called remote control because a standard electrical switch that controls an electrical load can be replaced with a Receiver switch, which can then be controlled from anywhere on the property using an X10 Transmitter as shown below.

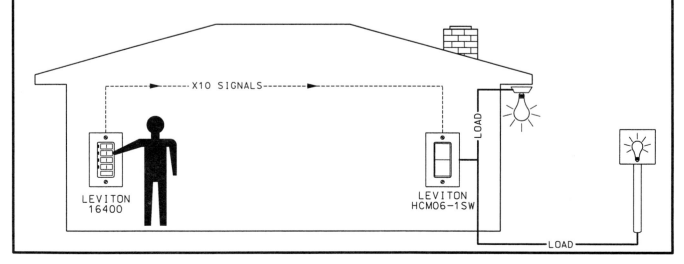

SYSTEM FEATURE 5
AUTOMATED SWIMMING POOL

The Home Controller is programmed to initiate the Pool Mode. This turns on the pool pump each day at 9:00 AM and allows the pool heater to turn ON if the thermostat is calling for heating. At 9:00 AM each day the Home Controller transmits the proper X10 signals over the power lines to wall Receiver switch 6371 to turn the pump ON. It also sends X10 signals to fixture appliance Receiver switch 6375 that will allow the gas heater to turn ON if it is calling for heat. The amount of heat received by the pool water is based on where the temperature adjustment knob is positioned on the heater panel. Feature 6 shown below, automatically controls two different water temperature set-points when heating either the pool or spa without having to walk to the heater to adjust the temperature knob each time. Repositioning of the water valves and control of the pump are also automated functions.

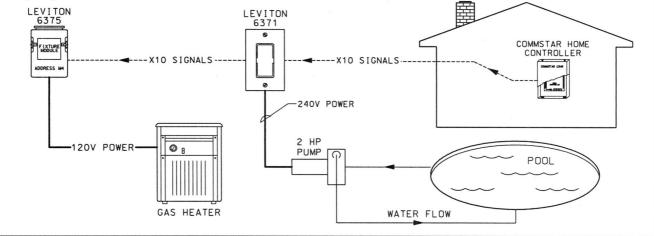

SYSTEM FEATURE 6
AUTOMATIC TEMPERATURE CONTROL OF THE POOL & SPA

The water from the pool is pumped through the heatpump to raise its temperature. The temperature of the water is sensed by an analog temperature sensor located in the return piping as shown, and is monitored by the Home Controller. The programming states that **IF** the temperature is less than 100 degree F, **THEN** close Relay Output 1 that is wired to the N.O. starter relay. This energizes the relay coil and closes the 240V contacts to **start** the heatpump. **IF** the water is equal to 102 degrees F, **THEN** open Relay Output 1 and **stop** the heatpump. To get this system to work properly, the temperature dial on the heatpump must be placed in the maximum position so the heater will turn ON each time power is applied.

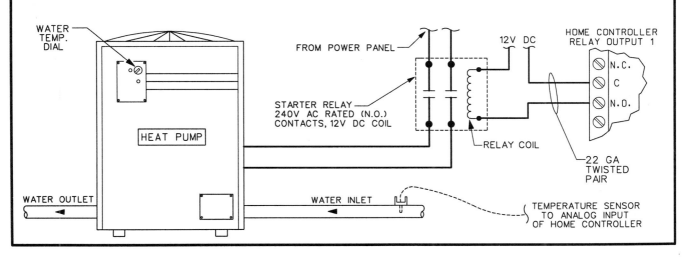

SYSTEM FEATURE 7
INITIATING THE ARRIVING HOME MODE FROM A VEHICLE

The Arriving Home Mode is one of the most useful modes to incorporate into a home automation system. There are a number of methods to activate this mode; however, in this example the homeowner approaches the home and pushes a keychain button. This transmits RF signals to the Street Smart wireless receiver located inside the home. When the receiver reads these signals, it closes a set of N.O. contacts that provides a Digital Input ON indication to the Home Controller. When the Home Controller reads this input, it will automatically turn ON exterior lighting, garage lights and one light in each room for safety only when it is after dark. It will then open the garage door, disarm the security system, open the drapes, turn ON the water heater, turn ON some music and control any other electrical load.

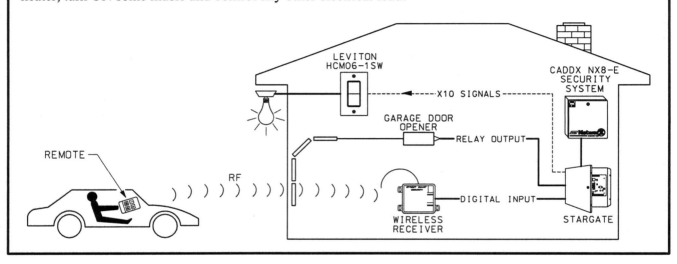

SYSTEM FEATURE 8
INITIATING THE ARRIVING HOME MODE BY OPENING A DOOR

The Arriving Home Mode can also be initiated by simply opening the garage door or front door of the home when arriving. The existing security system magnetic switches can be wired in series with a Digital Input of the Home Controller. Including the function of automatically disarming the security system by the action of simply opening the front door would not be appropriate for obvious reasons. The security system would need to be disarmed manually at the keypad. For the Home Controller to know whether to run the mode or not, the Leaving Home Mode sets a Flag in the programming, so only when the Flag is Set and the door is opened will the Arriving Home Mode be activated. This keeps the mode from running when an occupant is only going out front to get the newspaper.

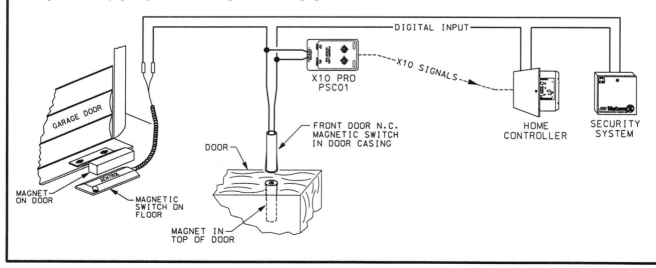

SYSTEM FEATURE 9
AUTOMATED WIRELESS LIGHTING CONTROL

An occupant entering a room is detected by wireless motion sensor MS13A. This sensor transmits RF signals through the air to be received by the TM751 Transceiver. The Transceiver is plugged into a standard power receptacle. The Transceiver then transmits X10-ON signals over the 120V power lines and is received by Receiver switch HCS10 that responds by turning the light ON. When the occupant leaves the room and motion is no longer detected over an adjustable period of time, the motion sensor will again send RF signals to the Transceiver that will send X10-OFF signals to turn the light OFF.

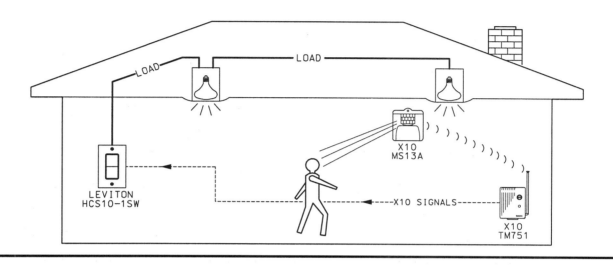

SYSTEM FEATURE 10
AUTOMATED WATER HEATER

The home's domestic water heater can be automated to save energy while the occupants are away from home. This can be accomplished by using the ELK-9100 switch. This device is ideal for this application because most electric water heaters will require more than 20 amps and this switch is rated for 30 amps. This unit is initiated ON and OFF by either receiving X10 commands from Transmitter TK184 or from the Home Controller as shown. It can also be controlled ON by a contact closure and OFF by opening the control circuit. In this example, X10 signals are sent by the Home Controller, or the Home Controller can use a Relay Output to turn the water heater ON and OFF. This feature is generally one of many control commands contained by the Leaving Home Mode, Arriving Home Mode, Morning Mode and Goodnight Mode.

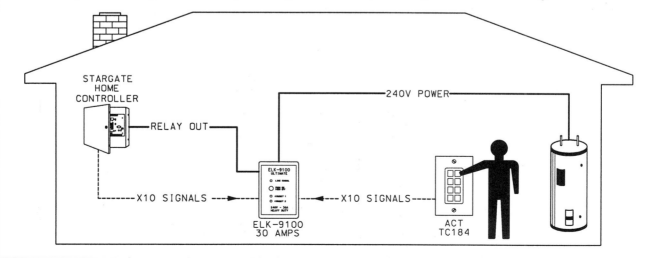

21

SYSTEM FEATURE 11
REMOTE CONTROL OF A/V EQUIPMENT FROM ANOTHER ROOM

An occupant can have full control of audio/video equipment located in a different room. The occupant can simply push the proper buttons on handheld remote PUR08 to send IR signals to IR Receiver ST539A. ST539A will then convert the IR signals to RF signal so they can travel through the walls to be received by the ST539B Powermid Receiver. The ST539B will then convert the RF signals back to IR signals before sending them through an emitter wire. These IR signals are received by the emitter that is adhered to the face of the appropriate audio/video component to be controlled.

SYSTEM FEATURE 12
AUTOMATED IRRIGATION SYSTEM

Based on the day of the week and time of day programmed into the Home Controller, the Home Controller will transmit X10-ON signals to the Zone 1 low voltage Receiver switch 6337. This switch will close the low voltage power circuit to open the Zone 1 solenoid valve. The Home Controller will then send X10-ON signals to the 240V Receiver switch XPS2 that will turn the sprinkler system well pump ON. After watering Zone 1 for ½ hour, the Home Controller will transmit X10-ON signals to the Zone 2 Receiver switch 6337 that will open the Zone 2 solenoid valve. The Home Controller will then send X10 OFF signals to close the Zone 1 solenoid valve. Alternating zones every ½ hour will automatically continue until the lawn receives sufficient water.

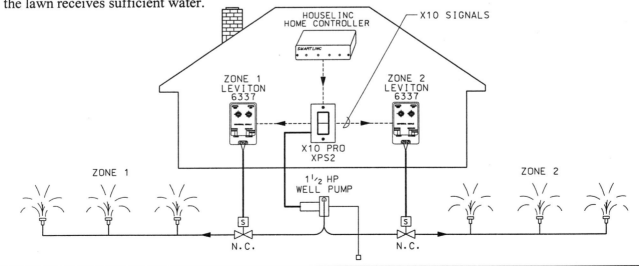

SYSTEM FEATURE 13
AUTOMATED LIGHTING AFTER DARK

PhotoCell Transmitter 6308 senses nightfall and transmits X10-ON signals to be received by Receiver switch HCM06 that turns the interior lights ON. A second set of X10-ON signals for a separate address is transmitted and received by Receiver switch RD101 to turn ON the exterior lights. A total of four different addresses are transmitted by the Photocell at nightfall. After a user selected number of hours from nightfall or in response to daylight, the PhotoCell will transmit X10-OFF signals to turn OFF the interior and exterior lights. Similar lighting control can be accomplished by using the plug-in Sundowner Controller PHC03 that also senses dusk and dawn. At dawn it transmits up to 4 different X10-OFF commands. It also doubles as an 8-button tabletop controller.

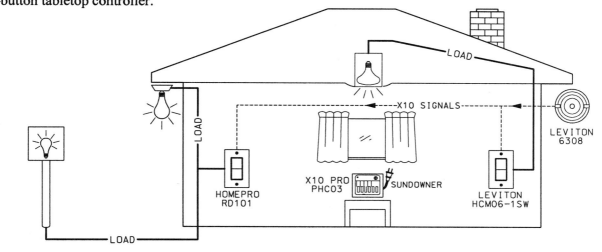

SYSTEM FEATURE 14
AUTOMATED WINDOW COVERINGS

From an easy chair an occupant can use the PHR03 push button Wireless Transmitter to send RF-OFF and then RF-ON signals to the PAT01 plug-in Transceiver. The Transceiver will then transmit X10-OFF and then ON signal over the power lines to turn ON Receptacle 6280. This provides power to the 'Add-A-Motor' transformer that automatically positions the drapes open. When the drapes reach the full open position, its internal limit switch will stop the 'Add-A-Motor'. To open the drapes the same OFF/ON control sequence must be followed. To stop the drapes some where between full open and full closed the user would simply remove power by turning OFF Receptacle 6280.

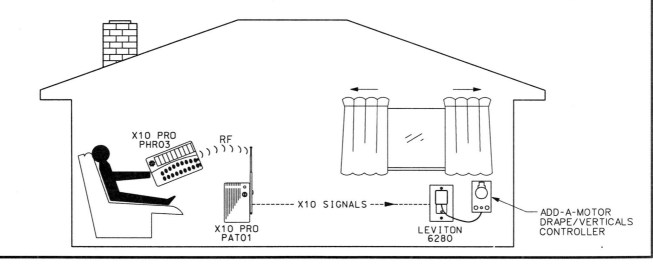

SYSTEM FEATURE 15
AUTOMATED MULTI-ZONE HVAC SYSTEM

An occupant will first select the heating and cooling temperature set-points for each Zone at the dedicated TS15 user interface or remotely. If either Zone is not meeting set-point, the air conditioner will be turned ON by the TX15 Zone control unit. Conditioned air will then flow to one or more Zones calling for cooling or heating through a normally open control damper supporting each Zone. When either the heating or cooling temperature set-point is satisfied in a particular Zone, the dedicated control damper will be closed by the multi-zone control panel. When both Zones are satisfied, the air conditioning system is turned OFF and the multi-zone panel ultimately opens each Zone control damper. The Home Controller is used to control the air conditioning system through a wide range of Modes.

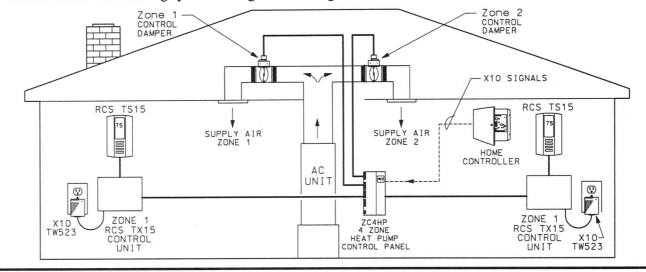

SYSTEM FEATURE 16
AUTOMATED VEHICLE DETECTION SYSTEM

A vehicle approaches the home and is detected by an underground probe. The Vehicle Alert control unit located in the equipment room will read this condition and close a set of normally open contacts wired to plug-in Transmitter 6330. The Transmitter will then send X10-ON signals over the power lines to the plug-in chime to provide an audible alert, and to UM506 plug-in Receiver switch to turn ON the CCTV camera. An occupant will then select the correct camera input on the TV to view the car and individuals. This will provide sufficient time to make sure the doors are locked or to call the police when danger is evident. This feature will also let the occupants know when friends or family members have arrived. In a more advanced system, a Home Controller is used to automatically turn the TV ON and select the assigned channel that corresponds to a specific CCTV camera.

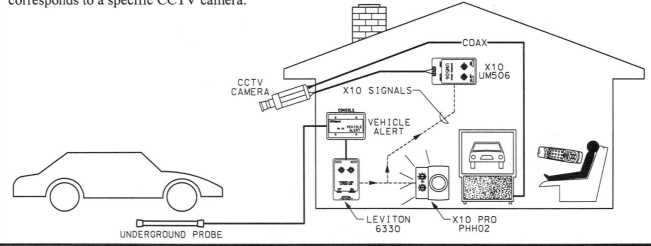

SYSTEM FEATURE 17
WATER LEAK DAMAGE PREVENTION SYSTEM

A water leak can occur at the clothes washer, water heater, sink, toilet, icemaker, etc. A dedicated water leak sensor called a Water Hound is located near each water fixture and will transmit RF signals to the WaterCop when a leak is detected. The WaterCop motorized shutoff valve will read these signals and shutoff the water supply to the home to avoid damage. This could occur while the occupants are away or at night while a sleep. The WaterCop should be installed in the main water supply pipe as close to the point of entry to the home as possible. When building a new home the owner has the option of pre-wiring the home. This will allow the homeowner to use a Home Controller with Digital Input and Relay Output capabilities and separate mechanical water sensors to economically cover more potential leak points.

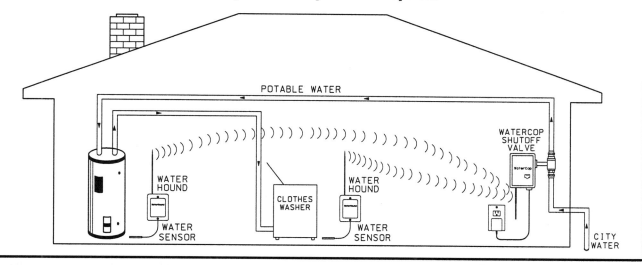

SYSTEM FEATURE 18
LIGHTS TURN ON IN THE HOME AS A VEHICLE APPROACHES

As a vehicle approaches the home, X10 security light motion detector 6417 will sense the vehicle and transmit X10-ON signals to Receiver switches HCS10 and HCM06 to turn ON interior and exterior lighting after dark. This mode is primarily used for security purposes if a vehicle approaches when the homeowner is away. When the homeowner arrives after dark, she will also light up the house for security purposes. After entering the home the occupant can control the lights as she wishes using wall Transmitter 16400. When she leaves the home when it gets dark and backs out of the driveway, interior lights will turn ON; however, she can easily use hand-held remote KR19A to send RF signals to Transceiver PAT01 to turn the lights OFF. More advanced methods do not allow interior lights to turn ON when the homeowner backs out of the driveway after dark.

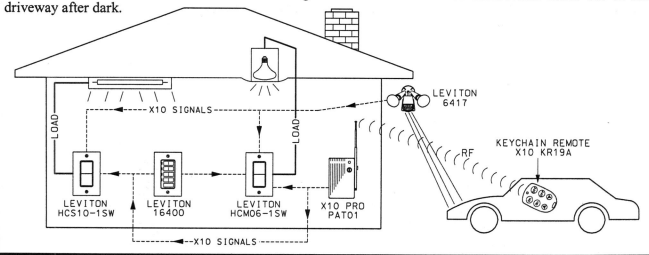

SYSTEM FEATURE 19
AUTOMATED FEEDWATER AND POOL PUMP CONTROL

A normally open float switch is installed inside a pipe off of the skimmer and is wired to plug-in Transmitter 6330 as shown. When the water level in the pool gets low, the float closes its internal switch. Transmitter 6330 will sense this circuit closure and transmit X10-ON signals over the power lines. Plug-in Receiver switch 6337 will respond by opening the solenoid valve. This will feed potable water to the suction side of the pump whether the pump is ON or OFF and will raise the water level in the pool. Once the desired level is established, the float switch will open and Transmitter 6330 will transmit X10-OFF signals to have Receiver switch 6337 close the feedwater solenoid valve. Basic pump run times are controlled by Timer PHT02. Please notice that a backflow **preventor** must be installed in this installation to avoid the potential of pool water entering the potable water system.

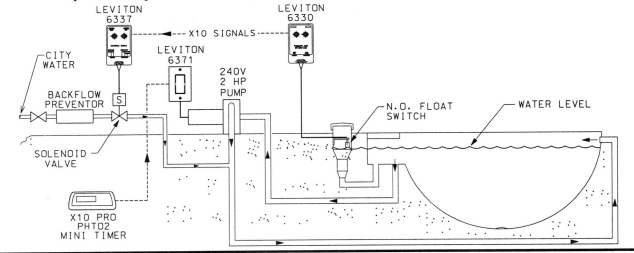

SYSTEM FEATURE 20
DISABLING POWER TO THE GARAGE DOOR OPENER FOR SECURITY

An occupant can shut OFF the power to the receptacle that powers the garage door to prevent a burglar from opening the door with an RF transmitting device. The occupant performs this function by simply pushing a button on Transmitter 12064W, that sends X10-OFF signals to Receiver receptacle PA011 to turn it OFF. This method is a remote control approach to removing power from the garage door opener; however, an automated approach would be to add this single function to the multitude of functions that make up the Leaving Home Mode, Arriving Home Mode, Good Night Mode and Vacation Mode. The Leaving Home Mode would turn OFF the Receiver receptacle 15 minutes after the mode is initiated to allow the owner time to leave. The Arriving Home Mode would turn the power back ON and open the garage door. It would also turn the power back OFF 15 minutes later to prevent a burglar from opening the door while the owner is at home.

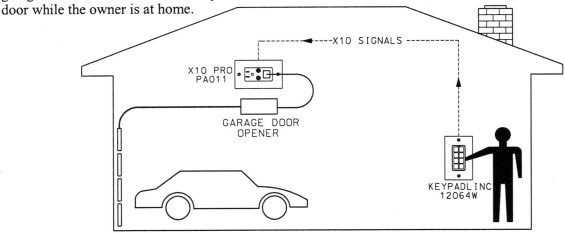

SYSTEM FEATURE 21
AUTOMATED SPRINKLER OPERATION USED AS A DETERRENT

An intruder enters the yard and is picked up by the wireless motion detector DM10A. This device sends RF signals to plug-in Transceiver TM751. The Transceiver will then transmit X10-ON signals to plug-in low voltage Receiver switch PUM01 to power the normally closed solenoid valve and flow water. At the same time Receiver switch XPS2 will turn ON the pump and the sprinkler system will turn ON. This can potentially discourage an intruder from breaking in. The homeowner will know that the sprinkler system was turned ON by the sound of the PHH02 chime. The sprinkler system can be turned OFF by pushing a button on Transmitter TC184. This system can also prevent dogs from leaving their deposits on the lawn.

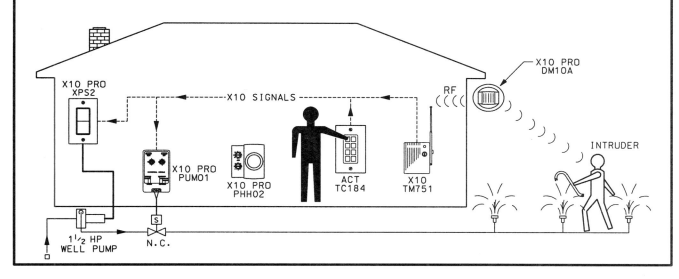

SYSTEM FEATURE 22
REMOTE CONTROL POOL AND PATIO LIGHTING

An occupant can remotely turn ON the pool & spa lights, patio lights and interior lighting from any location in the home by simply pushing the appropriate button on Transmitter 16400 labeled 'Mood lighting ON'. This is a basic example of having the ability to perform a 3-way control function from any location on the property without having to be wired in a 3-way configuration. In fact, if there is an existing switch used to control any 120V electrical load and the homeowner would like to add additional control capability from this location, he can simply remove the existing mechanical switch and replace it with a KeypadLinc 12063W. This device is basically a Receiver switch that controls the existing electrical load plus it is a Transmitter used to control other electrical loads on the property.

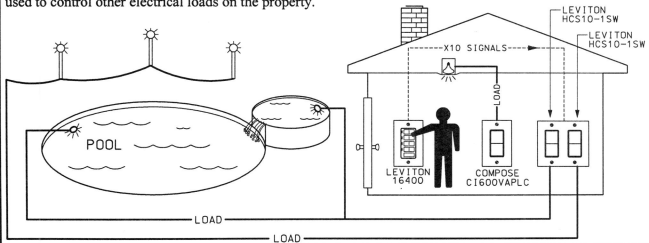

SYSTEM FEATURE 23
YEAR ROUND REMOTE CONTROLLED SHELF LIGHTING

Standard low voltage white Christmas lights can be used year round to light up the shelves for mood lighting scenes. This type of lighting provides just the right amount of light for the Romance Mode or to watch TV. All one needs to do is place a string of white Christmas lights back into the corner of a built-in shelf so it can't be seen from below, then plug in the light string into Receiver switch LM14A. The Receiver switch is then plugged into a standard wall receptacle. A Transceiver TM751 is also plugged into a wall receptacle within 50 feet of the RF Transmitter. The user can then control these lights as well as other electrical loads by using either the HCCUR Universal Remote or the 6320 16-button tabletop Transmitter. The LM14A plug-in Receiver switch is great for this application because it turns the lights ON by slowly brightening them from an off state and turns them OFF by slowly dimming them to an off state to provide a smooth mood lighting transition.

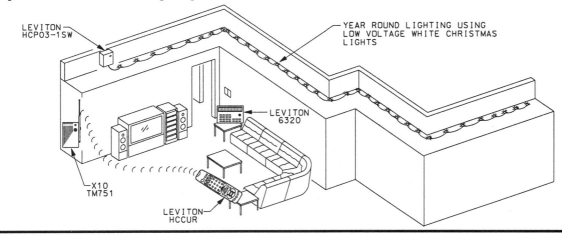

SYSTEM FEATURE 24
DOOR BELL ACTIVATES FOYER & PORCH LIGHTS AFTER SUNSET

This system is designed to turn ON the Foyer, Porch and exterior lighting when the doorbell button is pushed. Notice that the plug-in universal low voltage Receiver switch 6337 and the PowerFlash Module PSC01 are wired in series. This wiring is connected to the same terminals that the momentary push button doorbell switch is connected to on the doorbell. At dusk, Photocell 6308 transmits X10-ON signals to close Receiver switch 6337 that partially closes the low voltage circuit. When someone pushes the front door bell button, this fully closes the low voltage circuit. The plug-in PowerFlash Transmitter PSC01 will sense this circuit closure and transmits X10-ON signals to the two HCM06 Receiver switches to turn the lights ON. At sunrise the Photocell will transmit X10-OFF signals and open Receiver switch 6337 to reset the system for the next sunset. For this application the PowerFlash Module must be set to Input B, Mode 2.

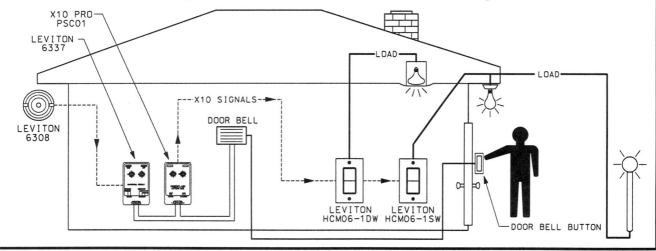

SYSTEM FEATURE 25
X10 SIGNAL COUPLER/BRIDGE INSTALLATION

A Phase Coupler is used to provide a less resistive path for X10 signals when travelling from one phase to another. Standard power for USA residential homes is 120V/240V split-phase service. This means that the home is fed by a quantity of two 120V single-phase power lines, 180 degrees out of phase from each other. Half of the house is powered by one phase while the other half is powered by the other phase. When a 240V load is wired, both phases are used. The Phase Coupler is installed in a single gang switch box next to the power distribution panel. It is wired to an available 15A circuit breaker as shown in this detail. For instance, when an occupant is transmitting X10 signals from in the Living Room, that is powered by Phase A, and she wants to control an electrical load powered by Phase B, the Phase Coupler will allow X10 signals to travel from Line A to Line B more effectively to provide a higher degree of system reliability.

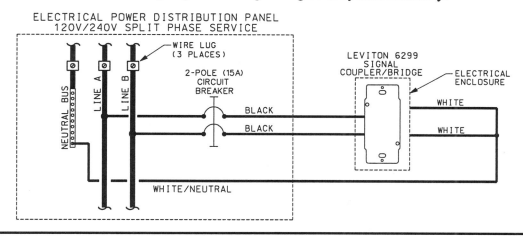

SYSTEM FEATURE 26
COUPLER/REPEATER INSTALLATION

The Leviton HCA02 Amplified Coupler Repeater is generally installed in homes that are 2500 square feet or larger or in any home that experiences low signal strength in certain areas of the home. This device couples the two phases in the same manner as the phase coupler shown above except this unit amplifies X10 signals from 100mv to 5V and repeats the signals for even greater X10 system reliability. This unit also provides a built-in test signal feature that simplifies troubleshooting. One LED shows that there are X10 signals on the power lines and the other LED shows an error condition. This device also has a test button that transmits X10 signals making it easy to verify signal strength with an X10 test indicator.

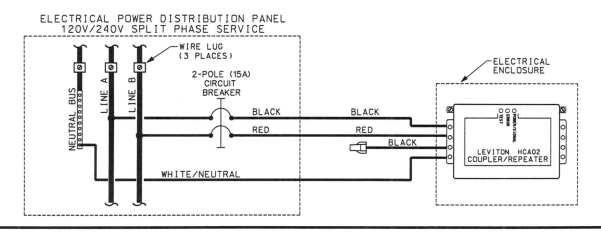

SYSTEM FEATURE 27
AMPLIFIED COUPLER/REPEATER

The ACT CR234 Amplified Coupler Repeater is generally installed in homes that are 3500 square feet or larger or in any home that experiences low signal strength in certain areas of the home. This device couples the two phases in the same manner as the phase coupler previously described except this unit amplifies and repeats signals with a higher signal output for even greater X10 system reliability. This unit also provides status LEDs on the front cover and is fuse protected (field replaceable). Internal dip switches can select special features. One feature allows signal carrying conductor signal to take priority over any other code being received. It can also receive at 0° or 30° and repeat or ignore repeated signal. It also handles preset dim commands and extended code.

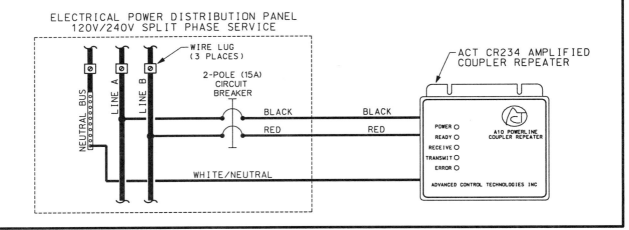

SYSTEM FEATURE 28
SIGNAL BLOCK, COUPLER, NOISE SUPPRESSOR INSTALLATION

The Leviton 6284 performs three functions. It is an X10 signal block that blocks X10 signals from entering the home from a neighbor's home served by the same power transformer. This unit also filters out electrical noise coming from outside the home. It is also a phase coupler that allows X10 signals to travel from one 120V phase to the other 120V phase with low resistance, which alleviates most system problems. Notice that the large Neutral cable is passed through the body of this device.

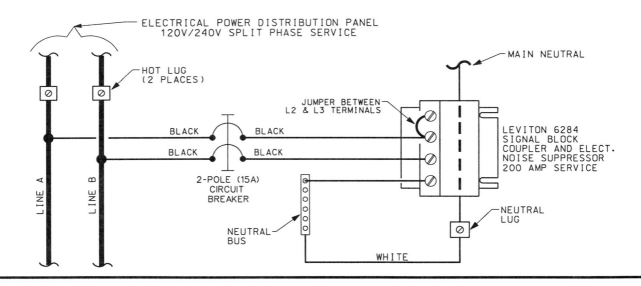

SYSTEM FEATURE 29
CATEGORY A & B WHOLE HOUSE SURGE SUPPRESSION

It is important to incorporate the appropriate whole house surge suppression equipment in a home especially when it contains Home Controllers, Sub-Controllers, Power-Line Carrier components, audio/video equipment and personal computers. A home should have a Category 'B' surge suppressor connected to either the electrical power meter panel located outside the home or to the power distribution panel located inside the home as shown. It is best to install the Category 'B' unit to the power meter panel because the grounding rod is close to this location, which is a less resistive path for the surge suppressor to throw the transient energy to ground. Category 'A' surge suppressors should be installed at each power receptacle that serves a Home Controller, audio/video equipment, personal computers and other plug-in electronic equipment.

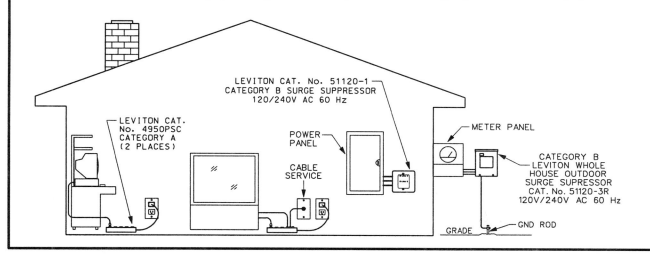

SYSTEM FEATURE 30
WHOLE HOUSE SURGE SUPPRESSOR INSTALLATION

The Leviton 51120-3R surge suppressor is a Category B3 device that is designed to be connected to the power meter panel located outside the home. It protects the home from transient energy and surges on the power lines that originate from outside the home that can damage electronic equipment. This unit is housed in a Nema 3R enclosure to protect the surge suppressor from the weather. This unit has a 640V combination wave rating and a UL rating of 800V. It is best to install a surge suppressor right at the power meter panel because the grounding rod is a short distance away, which allows the unit to throw the energy to ground faster and more effectively.

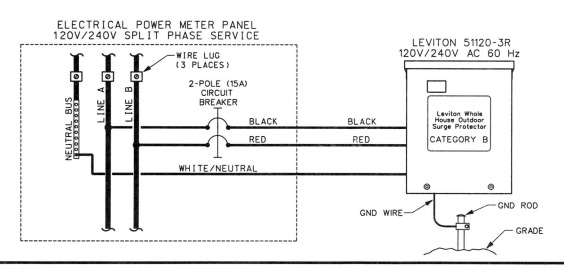

SYSTEM FEATURE 31
THE PANIC MODE

An occupant hears someone breaking into the home. She pushes the panic button on tabletop Transmitter MC460, which sends out X10-ON signals over the power lines to close the UM506 low voltage Receiver switch. This switch is connected to the Panic Zone terminals of the security system. When the Receiver switch closes, the security system senses this condition and alarms the security system. This activates the siren and strobe and automatically calls the security system monitoring company. The 6330 Burglar alarm interface is connected to the security system's siren terminals, so when the 6330 sense low voltage from this circuit, the 6330 transmits X10-ON signals to both HCM06 Receiver switches to turn all lights ON.

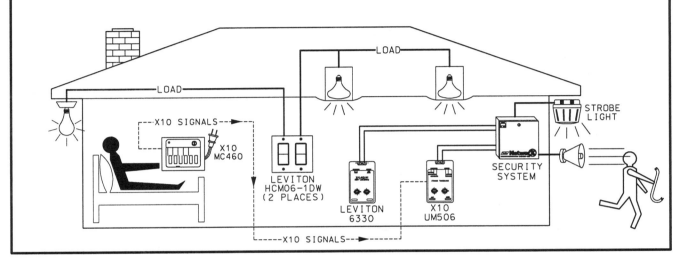

SYSTEM FEATURE 32
LOCK ALL DOORS AS PART OF THE GOOD NIGHT MODE

Doors in the home can be locked automatically by using electric door locks, a Home Controller, the SMST8 Transmitter and an integrated security system. When an occupant pushes the Transmitter button labeled 'Lock Doors', it will transmit X10-ON signals over the power lines to the Home Controller. Once the signals are received, the Home Controller will close a number of dedicated Relay Outputs wired to the electric door locks to energize the circuits, which will in turn lock the doors. Locking the doors is normally included as part of the Good Night Mode, Leaving Home Mode or Vacation Mode. All of the door locks in the home are locked immediately when initiating the Good Night Mode; however, when initiating the Leaving Home Mode or Vacation Mode, all the door locks except the exit door is locked. As the occupant opens the exit door to leave and then closes the door behind them, the Home Controller senses that the magnetic switch has closed, which tells the Home Controller to lock the door.

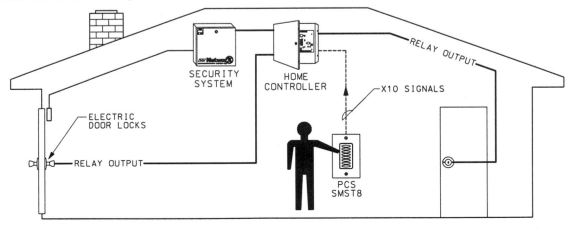

SYSTEM FEATURE 33
AUTOMATICALLY TURN ON LIGHTS AFTER SUNSET BY OPENING DOOR

This mode is designed to turn on lights only after dusk when arriving through the front door. The normally open magnetic contact switch at the door, plug-in low voltage Receiver switch PUM01 and plug-in Transmitter PSC01 are all wired in series as shown. At dusk Photocell 6308 Transmits X10-ON signals and closes Receiver switch PUM01. This partially closes the circuit but does not activate the PSC01 Transmitter. When the homeowner arrives home and opens the front door, the normally open switch closes, which now fully closes the circuit. This condition is sensed by Transmitter PSC01, which transmits X10-ON signals to Receiver switch HCM06 and LM14A to turn the lights ON. When the sun comes up, Photocell 6308 will transmit X10-OFF signals and open Receiver switch PUM01 to reset the system for the next evening. The lights will need to be manually turned OFF or remotely turned OFF from wall Transmitter 12064W. Transmitter PSC01will need to be set to Input B, Mode 2.

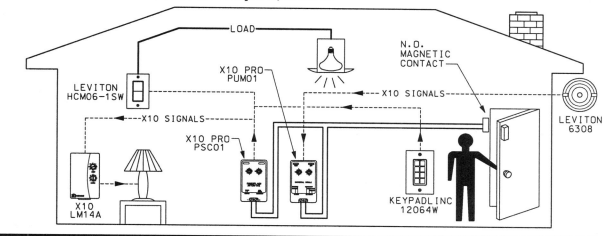

SYSTEM FEATURE 34
TURN OFF POTENTIALLY DANGERIOUS APPLIANCES

As part of the Leaving Home Mode and Good Night Mode it is generally appropriate to turn OFF Receiver receptacles that power appliances that contain heating elements. These types of devices can fail and potential cause a fire. This includes electrical loads such as toasters, electric ovens, coffeepots, curling irons, etc. In this simplified diagram, the occupant initiates one of the modes by pushing a button on Transmitter SMST6. This sends X10 signals to the Home Controller to tell it to initiate one of the modes. As part of the many individual functions provided by each mode, both 6280 Receiver receptacles along with other Receiver switches are turned OFF. The Arriving Home Mode and Good Morning Mode will automatically turn all Receiver receptacles back ON that were turned OFF by the Leaving Home Mode and the Good Night Mode.

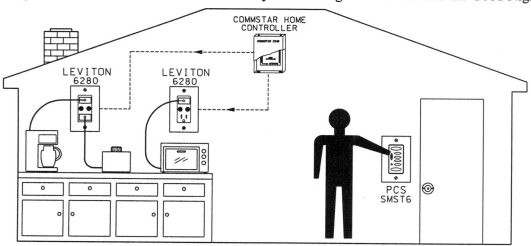

SYSTEM FEATURE 35
READY MOTEL ROOM FOR OCCUPANCY

A motel clerk located in the main lobby checks in a customer and pushes the appropriate buttons on the SC503 16-button tabletop Transmitter. This sends X10-ON signals to the designated room the includes three different types of Receiver switches. These devices ultimately turn ON the air conditioning, ceiling fans and lights to ready the room before the occupant enters. In this particular application all three types of Receiver switches are set to the same address. When the occupant checks out of the room, the clerk can simply send X10-OFF commands to make sure these electrical loads are all OFF. This mode can save a great deal of energy, which will pay for the system components within a relatively short period of time.

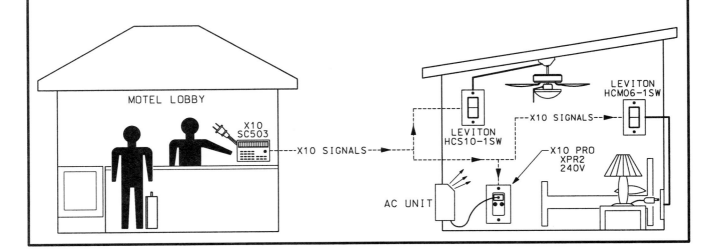

SYSTEM FEATURE 36
WIRELESS REMOTE CONTROL OF ELECTRICAL LOADS FROM LONG DISTANCE

Normally one would control electrical loads from a distance by using a telephone controller or the Internet; however, there are applications where there are no phones or computers in the location of the devices to be controlled. In this case an individual can use and RF Transmitter and Receiver with a range of up to 10 miles to perform these functions. All the user needs to do is push a button on the RF Transmitter to send RF signals to the RF Receiver. When the RF Receiver receives these signals, it response by closing a set of internal N.O. low voltage control contacts. This will power the relay coil, which will close a 120V power circuit to turn the lights ON. In cases where the RF Receiver and relay components are not located inside a building for protection from the whether, the RF Receiver and relay combination should be installed in a Nema 3R or 4X enclosure.

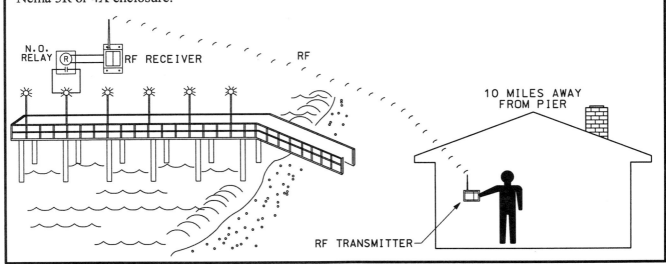

SYSTEM FEATURE 37
START AIR COMPRESSOR AND TURN ON SHOP LIGHT REMOTELY

In this application the homeowner has a regular schedule of spending most days working in his shop to make a living. In the morning before work he pushes a button labeled 'Shop ON' at Transmitter SMST8. This transmits X10-ON signals to remotely turn ON the 240V, 20 amp Receiver receptacle 6298 to power the compressor, so it will be up to pressure when he is ready to work. The X10-ON signals will also turn ON the lights in the shop by turning ON Receiver switch 6291. These control functions can also be included as part of the Good Morning Mode. To make sure the shop lights are turned OFF at the end of the day, X10-OFF signals can be part of the functions performed by the After Work Mode.

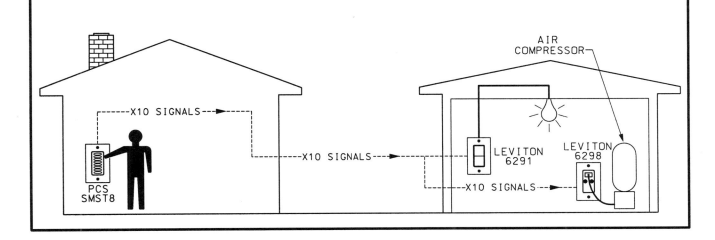

SYSTEM FEATURE 38
AUTOMATED PROPERTY ACCESS GATE, LIGHTS AND CCTV CAMERA

The property access gate area is an interesting portion of the home automation system. This sub-system includes control of the property access gate, CCTV surveillance and exterior lighting. When the occupants arrive home, they push a secure RF Transmitter button in the vehicle to open the gate. The car is kept safe from damage by the embedded 'safety loop' that detects a car within the gate's path, so it will not accidentally close on the car prematurely. When a vehicle leaves the home the gate will be opened automatically by the exit loop. The exterior lights will also turn ON at sunset and turn OFF at sunrise automatically by the Home Controller each day. Visitors will have to call on the property access phone for an occupant to open the gate. When the gate is opened without the approval of an occupant, the normally open magnetic switch as shown, will close and send a Digital Input to the Home Controller. It responds by sounding the security alarm and initiates an audible message over the whole house audio system to notify the occupants of the location where the intrusion has occurred.

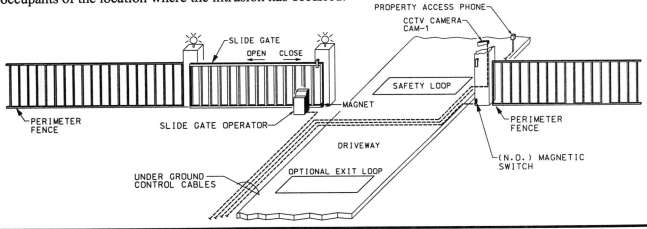

35

SYSTEM FEATURE 39
WIRELESS MAIL ALERT USED TO ANNOUNCE THE MAIL ARRIVAL

When the mailman arrives and opens the mailbox, the wireless RF Transmitter adhered to the mail box door senses motion and responses by transmitting RF signals for the 'Mail Alert Receiver' to receive. This notifies the occupants that the mail has arrived. The transmitter and receiver can be located as far as 300 feet away. Another use for this system is to alert the occupants of possible tampering of the mailbox if it sounds during an abnormal time of day when mail is not delivered. In new construction the homeowner has the option of pulling burial cable from the Home Controller location to the mailbox and install a standard security magnetic switch on the mail box and the magnet on the mail box door. When the door is opened this will send a Digital Input to the Home Controller and it will respond by sending out a voice response over the whole house A/V system that may say, "mail has arrived". If it is an abnormal time of day or at night and the mailbox is opened, a voice response for this condition can also be initiated.

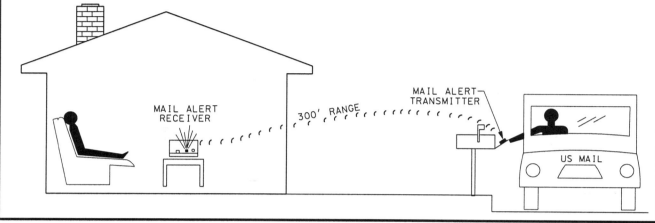

SYSTEM FEATURE 40
AUTOMATED CEILING FAN WHEN TEMPERTURE IS OVER 80°F

In this diagram notice that the plug-in Transmitter PSC02, the plug-in Receiver switch UM506 and the temperature alert sensor are all wired in series. This means that the Receiver switch and temperature sensor must both close their contacts before the light will turn ON. An occupant walks into a room and is sensed by the wireless motion sensor PMS02. The motion sensor responses by transmitting RF signals to plug-in Transceiver TM751, which transmits X10 signals over the power lines to close Receiver switch UM506. If the temperature in the room is over 80 degrees F, for instance, the temperature sensor contacts will completely close the circuit. This condition is sensed by plug-in Transmitter PSC01 that transmits X10 signals to Receiver switch HCS10 to turn the fan ON. If the temperature is below 80 degree F, the fan will not turn ON. In new construction where wire can be pulled, one would incorporate the method shown in System Feature 132.

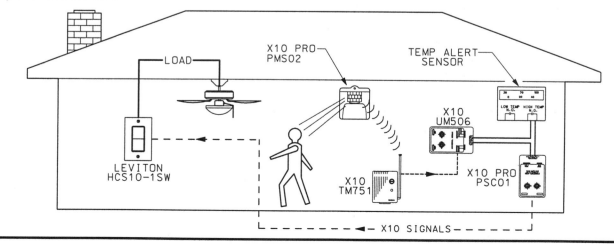

SYSTEM FEATURE 41
TAKE IN FRESH AIR WHEN CO2 LEVEL IS HIGH

During periods of time when there are an abnormal number of individuals in the home like during a party, the CO2 level in the home can rise and cause a stuffy undesirable environment. To solve this problem a CO2 sensor can be installed along with a few other control components. When the CO2 level rises above 1000 PPM, the CO2 sensor's internal contacts will close. This condition is sensed by Transmitter 6330, which sends X10 signals over the power lines to Receiver switch 6337 to open the N.C. outside air damper. X10-ON signals are also received by the thermostat to turn ON the air conditioning. This will draw fresh outside air into the home and lower the CO2 level. CO2 is relieved through a relief damper in the ceiling as shown. When a Home Controller is incorporated, an analog CO2 sensor can be used along with a RS485 thermostat and hardwired control damper.

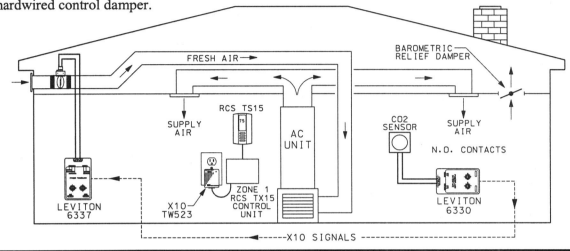

SYSTEM FEATURE 42
LIGHTS FLASH TO NOTIFY PARENTS WHEN PHONE RINGS

In families that have small children, parents want to avoid waking up their children during their daily naps and during the night. To be able to receive phone calls without waking them up, we need to alert the parents that the phone is ringing in a way that does not make noise. To perform this function all of the phone ringers must be turned off. A double phone plug adapter is used to install a second phone line connected to a plug-in PF284 Transmitter. When the phone rings, the PF284 Transmitter senses the voltage and sends X10-ON signals to specific Receiver switches that flash the lights ON & OFF. This quietly alerts mother that the phone is ringing. In this particular application the PF284 must be set to Input 'A' Mode 2.

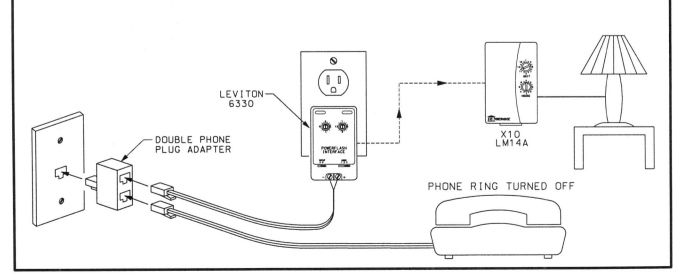

SYSTEM FEATURE 43
CONTROL ELECTRICAL LOADS FROM A WIRELESS WALL TRANSMITTER

In this feature the homeowner can have a 4-button wall Transmitter anywhere in the home without having to install another switch box with an additional gang for a wired-in Transmitter. Another reason why one would use an RF Transmitter PHW04D is if a neutral wire was not available in an existing switch box location to install a wired-in Transmitter. To remotely control electrical loads, the occupant would push the appropriate RF Transmitter button to send RF signals to Transceiver TM751. The Transceiver would then send X10-ON signals over the power lines to the proper Receiver switch to control the desired electrical load. If there is a neutral wire available in a desired switch box location and the installer does not want to replace the existing switch box to provide an additional gang, he could remove the existing standard switch and replace it with a KeypadLinc 12064W. This device is basically a Receiver switch and a Transmitter all in one. This means that it will be able to switch the existing electrical load or perform dimming functions and allow the user to control any other electrical load using the remaining buttons.

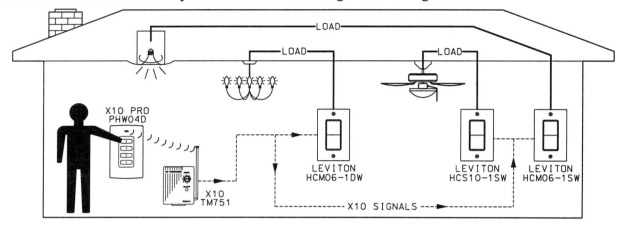

SYSTEM FEATURE 44
REMOTE CONTROL OF ELECTRICAL LOADS USING THE PHONE

This feature is powerful because any electrical load on the property can be controlled at home or anywhere in the world. For instance, if an occupant would like to turn ON the ceiling fan, she would pick-up the phone and punch in *23. The symbol * is for an ON command and # is for an OFF command. The number 2 phone button also has letter 'C' on it for 'ceiling' and the number 3 button has the letter 'F' for 'fan'. The same control logic can be used for the other loads. In a whole house automation system that incorporates a Home Controller, the first letter would indicate what Zone or area of the home that the electrical load is in and the second letter would identify the specific electrical load to control within a Zone. To control loads from outside the home, an occupant would call the home, punch in the access code and then punch in the desired control commands. Confirmation that a control function has occurred is indicated by an audible response.

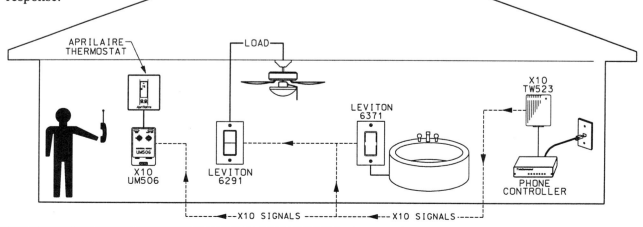

SYSTEM FEATURE 45
STRUCTURED WIRING SYSTEM FUTURE PROOFS THE HOME

A structured wiring system is primarily used to distribute telephone service, cable TV service, satellite TV service, Internet service and to network the PCs. This system is also installed for the purpose of future proofing the home so when new technology is developed, the system can support it. The whole system centers around a Structured Wiring Distribution Panel that generally contains a service input hub, a telephone hub, a coax TV hub or satellite TV hub and an Internet networking hub. One of the many great features provided by this panel is that if the homeowner wants to move electronic equipment from one room to another, patch cords on the distribution panel can be reconfigured to direct service to the correct location. Wire Bundles are pulled through the home to each service receptacle location during construction. Wire Bundles usually contain two Category 5 cables, two RG6 coax cables and two fiber optic cables. Even telephone system panels can be integrated in with the Distribution Panel to provide a full range of telephone system features. Refer to the Structure Wiring Design Manual shown at the back of this book for detailed information on how to design a Structured Wiring System for your home.

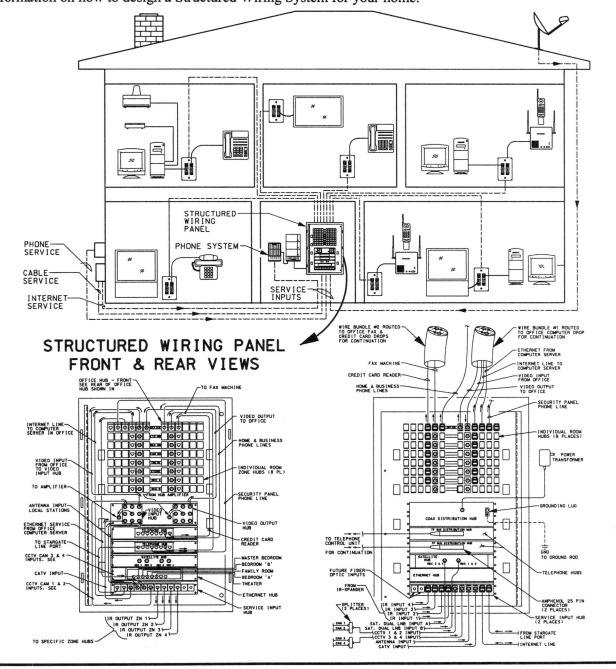

STRUCTURED WIRING PANEL FRONT & REAR VIEWS

SYSTEM FEATURE 46
THE CHRISTMAS MODE

The Christmas Mode is a nice mode to incorporate into a Home Automation System because it makes the home look so good and is easy to control. All an occupant needs to do is push a button labeled 'Christmas' on Transmitter 16400. This will send X10-ON signals to all Receiver switches set to the same address to turn the lights ON. This mode can also be turned ON automatically on the correct days of the year exactly at sunset by using the proper Home Controller. For example, the Home Controller can be programmed to begin turning ON the Christmas lights December 1 of each year at sunset, which the Home Controller tracks all year long. The Home Controller can also be programmed to leave the Christmas light Receiver switches OFF beginning on January 1 of each year.

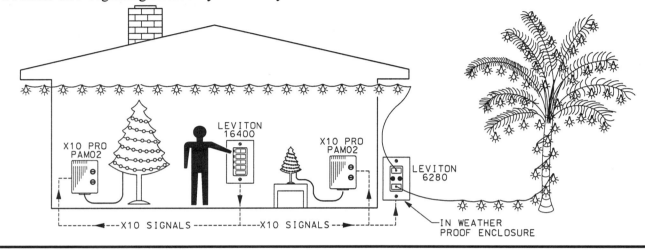

SYSTEM FEATURE 47
REMOTELY TURN OFF TV AND VIDEO GAME RECEPTACLE DURING STUDY TIME

This mode provides the parents with some control over the period of time that the children need to do their homework. All a parent needs to do is push the 'Study' button on Transmitter 12064W to send X10-OFF signals to wall Receiver switch receptacle 6280. This will remove power from the TV and video game unit. Automatic OFF and ON control of this feature can be setup by using Timer MT10A; however, the Timer will also turn OFF the Receiver switch on the weekends when homework is not required. Another option is to incorporate this mode into the schedule of a Home Controller, which can be programmed to turn the power OFF for study time and then back ON for entertainment. Power OFF will occur only on the correct days of the week and not on any of the holidays throughout the year.

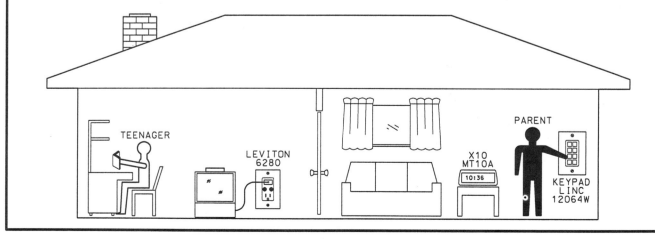

SYSTEM FEATURE 48
REMOTELY CONTROLLED FIREPLACE

An occupant can have remote control or automatic control of a fireplace with electronic ignition by using either the *Stargate* or *CommStar* Home Controller. Other controllers could be used; however, we are using an 8-button LCD Keypad, which is hardwired and communicates through an RS-485 connection. We could use X10 components to accomplish this feature; however, an added level of dependability is justified for this application. To start the fireplace, the occupant would bring up a screen on the LCD Keypad that contains the fireplace Icons and select fireplace ON. This command will tell the Home Controller to close an I/O Relay Output to start the fireplace. We recommend that a Master Electrician make the correct connections to the fireplace circuitry.

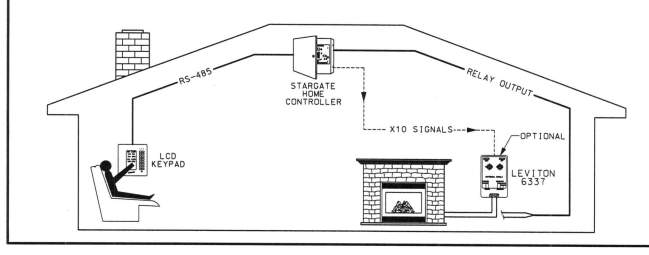

SYSTEM FEATURE 49
REMOTELY CONTROLLED DOOR SYSTEM

Individuals that are handicapped can benefit from home control features in many ways. One way is to incorporate 'Open Sesame' door actuators in the home. A handicapped person can use a keychain remote that is on their person at all times to control the doors. In this feature the individual pushes one button on the remote to send RF-ON signals to plug-in Transceiver 6314. This device will transmit X10-ON signals over the power lines to low voltage Receiver switch 6337. The Receiver switch will in turn close a low voltage circuit to power the door actuator and open the door. The door can be closed using the remote; however, there is also a feature that automatically closes the door after a time delay.

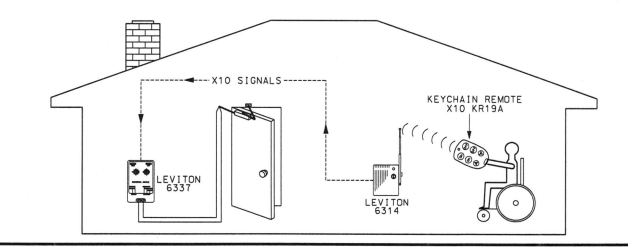

SYSTEM FEATURE 50
AUTOMATED AIR CONDITIONING BOOSTER FAN

In this home the existing air conditioner does not provide sufficient airflow for certain rooms in the home. The addition of a booster fan may solve this problem and can be controlled as follows: When the thermostat is not satisfied, it will close a 24 volt control circuit to start the air conditioning equipment. This will apply voltage to the N.O. relay coil and close the relay contacts. This closure is sensed by Transmitter PF284 that transmits X10-ON signals to Receiver switch UM506. This switch closes a low voltage circuit to power the booster fan. When the temperature set-point is satisfied, the thermostat circuit will open and the PF284 will send X10-OFF signals to open the Receiver switch and turn the fan OFF.

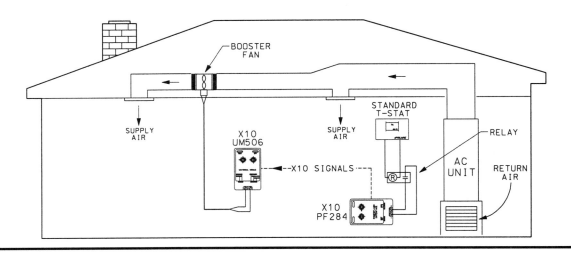

SYSTEM FEATURE 51
CONTROL THE HOME OVER THE INTERNET

In this feature the *Stargate* Home Controller and the *Web-Xpander* are used. With this equipment the homeowner can get on the Internet at work or anywhere in the world to have complete control of all electrical loads in the home. The user can also check the status of the security system or any other electrical loads on the property. Thermostats can be adjusted, lights can be turned ON/OFF, drapes can be repositioned and doors can be opened for service personnel. The spa can even be started so it will be ready upon arrival. The home can also be controlled from a pocket PC. In addition, the *Web-Xpander* can send E-mails in response to any condition.

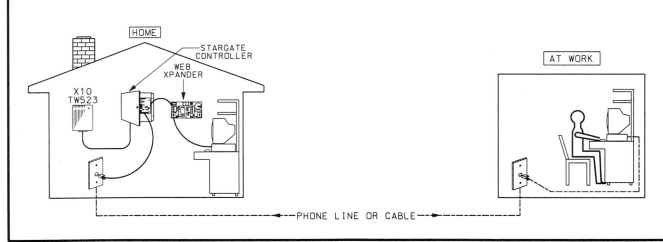

42

SYSTEM FEATURE 52
COOK DINNER AT HOME WHILE AT WORK

The crock-pot needs to be turned ON and OFF at the appropriate times to avoid under cooking or over cooking dinner. This can be performed by using an X10 Pro Timer PHT02 or by calling home and using the Telephone Controller to access control of the crock pot. Once system access has been established by phone, the Telephone Controller can be used to transmit X10-ON and OFF signals through Interface Module TW523. This places X10 signals on the power lines to turn ON-OFF Receiver receptacle 6280 to apply or remove power. When installing X10 type Receiver receptacles, do not replace GFI receptacles. We do not recommend the use of load sense X10 receptacles because they can be turned ON prematurely by surges or brown outs on the power lines.

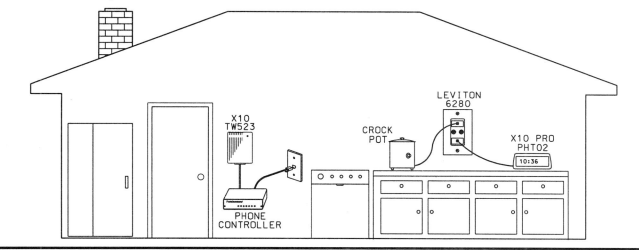

SYSTEM FEATURE 53
PERSONAL ASSITANCE SYSTEM

This feature provides an individual with assistance if an emergency should arise. All the individual needs to do is push a button on the waterproof pendant that they carry with them at all times. This will send RF signals to the Personal Assistance Console. Once the signals are received, the console will call up to as many as four telephone number if the first three do not answer and when a phone is answered a pre-recorded message will play. When the person receiving the call pushes a button on the phone, they will be able to listen in to the distressed person's home through the console mounted microphone. This unit will also activate X10 Receiver switches if desires.

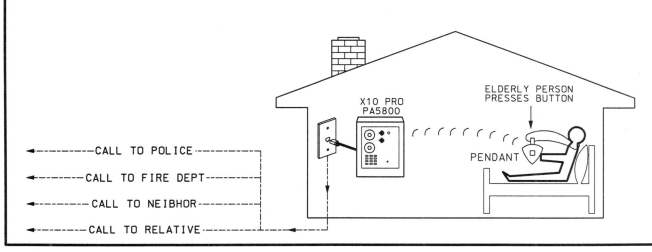

43

SYSTEM FEATURE 54
AUTOMATED LAWN CHEMICAL INJECTION SYSTEM

This feature keeps the lawn looking great and bug free. This is because the homeowner never has to remember to physically apply fertilizer, herbicides or pesticides again. These chemicals are applied automatically through the lawn sprinkler system based on a time schedule programmed into the Home Controller. These chemicals should be applied based on the chemical manufacturer's recommendations. When the schedule states that it is time to apply one or more chemicals the next time the lawn is scheduled to receive water, the appropriate solenoid valves are opened. These valves are controlled by Relay Outputs from the Home Controller, which allows each chemical to enter the suction side of the pump and be pumped to the sprinkler heads.

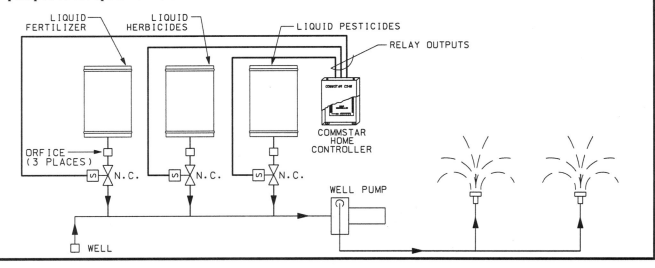

SYSTEM FEATURE 55
PARENT AT WORK VIEWS CHILD AND BABY SITTER AT HOME

Mother is at work and is curious about how the new baby sitter and child are doing. Her computer is equipped with a remote surveillance card that is installed in the PCI slot of her Pentium IV PC. She gets on the Internet and goes to a personnel web site by entering a password. After entering the system and software she is able to view a few areas of the home through various hidden cameras. When she selects the family room clock camera, she notices that the child is crying and the babysitter is yelling at the child. After she watches for a few minutes, the situation does not improve, so she calls home to talk to the baby sitter without letting her know that she is being watched. The call is to basically try and calm down the situation before mother leaves work to confront the babysitter in person.

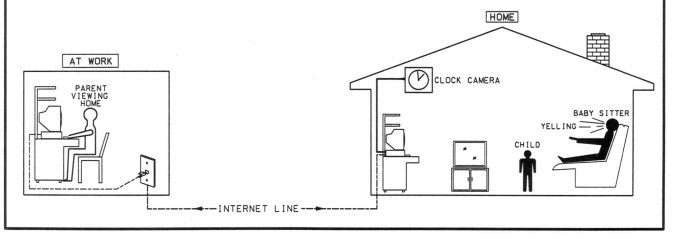

SYSTEM FEATURE 56
AUTOMATED ELECTRIC BLANKET

Electric blankets can be automatically turned on by the Good Night Mode, so the bed is warm when homeowner gets in. This feature is easy to incorporate into this mode by simply installing either a 6280 Receiver receptacle or a PAM02 plug-in appliance Receiver switch. A Receiver receptacle with the load sense feature is not recommended, because they can be triggered ON prematurely by electrical power surges or brownouts. Always check if the Receiver switch rating can handle the wattage required by the electrical load before using it.

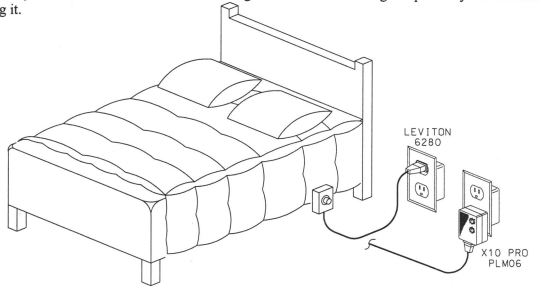

SYSTEM FEATURE 57
AUTOMATED OVERFLOW PREVENTION DUE TO EXCESSIVE RAIN FALL

In some areas of the country there are times when it can rain up to 3 inches an hour. This can cause flooding in the pool area, which I have experienced personally in Central Florida. There is generally an overflow pipe installed off the bottom of the skimmer to drain off water; however, the ground can get saturated and not absorb water fast enough. To remedy this problem a N.O. float switch is installed in a short 6" diameter pipe off the skimmer that is capped as shown. When the water raises to a critical level, the float will rise and the switch will close. This will initiate a Digital Input that is read by the Home Controller. The Home Controller will then close a Relay Output to close a low voltage power circuit that opens a Jandy drain valve. Another Relay Output and a starter relay starts the pump to drain off the excess water to the lowest elevation on the property. When the water level falls in the pool, the float switch opens and the Home Controller will open both Relay Outputs to stop the pump and close the drain valve.

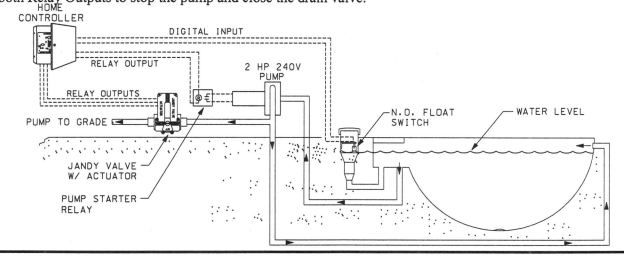

SYSTEM FEATURE 58
CONTROL THE SPA TEMPERATURE FROM THE SPA

In this feature the people in the spa do not need to get out to adjust the temperature knob on the heater when the water feels to hot or not hot enough. To have this feature work, the homeowner needs to set the thermostat temperature knob up high to make sure the heater comes on when control power is applied to the heater. While in the spa, the womon feels that the water is getting too hot. The gentlemen grabs the hand-held remote, pushes the OFF button to sends RF signals to plug-in Transceiver PAT01 located in the home. The Transceiver then sends X10-OFF signals over the power lines to Fixture Receiver switch 6375. This turns OFF the power to the heater control circuit, which turns OFF the heater. When the water become too cool, the 'Heater ON' button can be pushed on the remote.

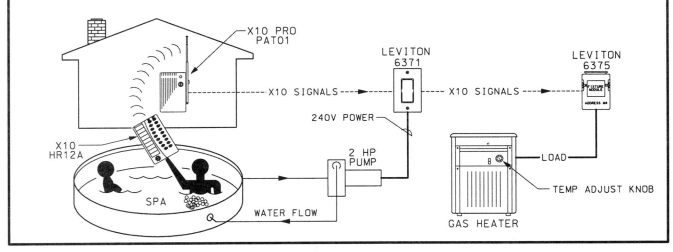

SYSTEM FEATURE 59
AUTOMATICALLY CLOSE GARAGE DOOR AT SUNSET

At dusk the 6308 Photocell transmits X10-ON signals over the power lines to the plug-in low voltage Receiver switch UM506. This momentarily closes the switch and initiates the garage door closed only if the door is in the open position. Notice that Receiver switch UM506 is wired in series with the N.O. magnetic switch at floor level. If the door is open, the magnetic switch is closed. This allows the circuit to fully close when Receiver switch UM506 is closed by the Photocell, which will close the garage door. If it is dusk and the door is already closed, the magnetic switch maintains the circuit open, and Receiver switch UM506 will not open the door. Set the UM506 to momentary closure, relay only.

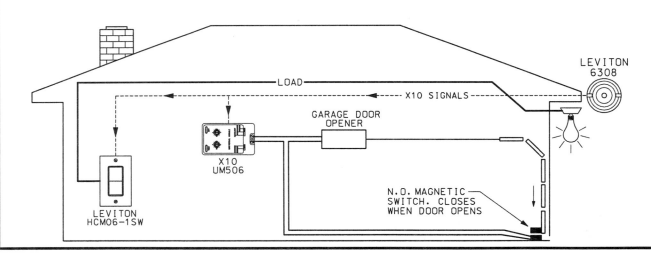

46

SYSTEM FEATURE 60
WARM UP THE SPA ON THE WAY HOME AFTER A HARD DAYS WORK

CELL PHONE

IN ROUTE HOME

A man has a hard day at work and would like to get in the spa to relax upon arrival. He picks up the cell phone and calls home. After the phone is answered by the Telephone Controller, he enters a password to access the system. Once he accesses the system, he presses buttons *77. This sends X10-ON commands to Receiver switch XPS2 and Receiver switch 6375 to turn ON both the pump and the pool/spa heater. To have this feature work, the homeowner needs to set the thermostat temperature knob up to the high position to make sure the heater comes on when control power is applied.

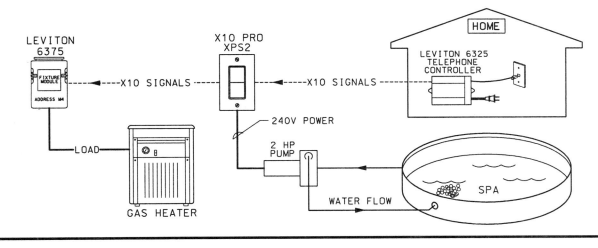

SYSTEM FEATURE 61
AUTOMATED CONTROL OF THE HVAC SYSTEM

The user has the ability to have complete control of the Heating, Cooling and Ventilation system as well as all other home automation control functions directly from his easy chair. By using the LCD Keypad with an RS-485 connection, ACSII communications is received by the *Stargate* or *Commstar*. The Home Controller will then communicate to the *RCS* TR36 HVAC controller. The user has the option of selecting individual control functions like the Cooling Mode, Heating Mode, Ventilation Mode or system OFF function. The user can also select from a wide range of temperature set-points. Any of these HVAC control functions can be a part of a variety of modes to perform the desired settings for different occasions. This keeps the user from having to select individual setting each time.

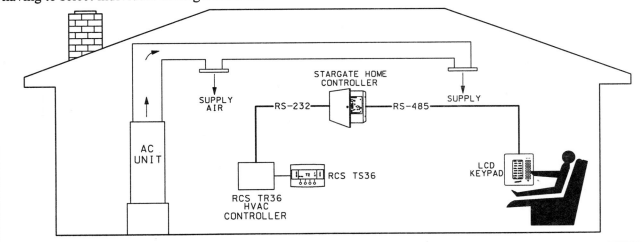

SYSTEM FEATURE 62
KNOW WHEN SOMEONE IS APPROACHING THE HOUSE

In this feature an intruder is in the backyard and is approaching the home. The security light motion sensor 6417 detects this individual and transmits X10-ON signals over the power lines to activate chime SC546A. This alerts the occupants that someone is approaching. For the hearing impaired person living in the home, plug-in Receiver switch 6337 that is wired to plug-in Transmitter 6330 closes. The Transmitter senses this closure and transmits X10-Flash signals to Receiver switch HCM06 that will flash the lights. When the motion sensor no longer senses motion, Receiver switch 6337 will remain closed and the lights will continue to flash. An occupant can override the flashing lights by pushing a button on Transmitter 16400 to open Receiver switch 6337 and maintain the lights ON.

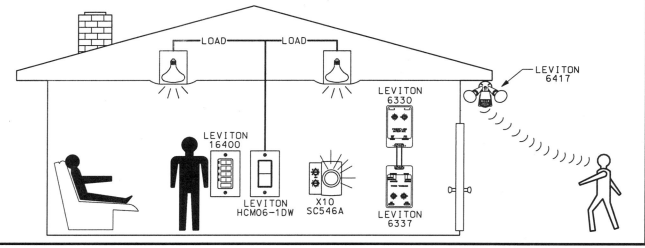

SYSTEM FEATURE 63
CHIME & VIDEO RESPONSE THAT SOMEONE HAS ARRIVED

In this feature someone is approaching the front door. The hardwired motion sensor detects this individual and sends a Digital Input to the Home Controller. The Home Controller will then Transmit X10-ON signals to activate Chime PHH02 for and audible warning. At the same time the Home Controller closes a Relay Output to power the low voltage surveillance camera. The Home Controller will also have the IR-Xpander send the proper IR signals to automatically turn the TV ON and select the proper video input. This will allow the homeowner to instantly view the person approaching before they reach the front door.

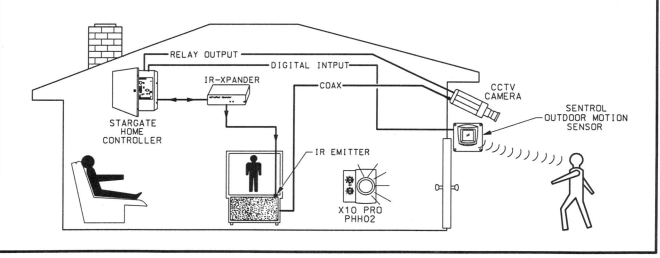

SYSTEM FEATURE 64
CONTROL THE TEMPERATURE IN THE HOME FROM YOUR BED

An occupant that is in bed at night, or in bed when sick can have full control over the heating, cooling and ventilation system without getting out of bed. Functions can be provided without having to pull hardwires during the installation. All they need to do is push the assigned remote button to select the heating mode, cooling mode, ventilating mode and a wide range of temperature set-points. To operate the system, the appropriate RF signals are sent by hand-held remote PHR03 that are received by plug-in Transceiver PAT01. The Transceiver then sends X10-ON signals over the power lines to X10 Interface Module TW523 that translates X10 signals to the RCS TX-15 HVAC System Controller.

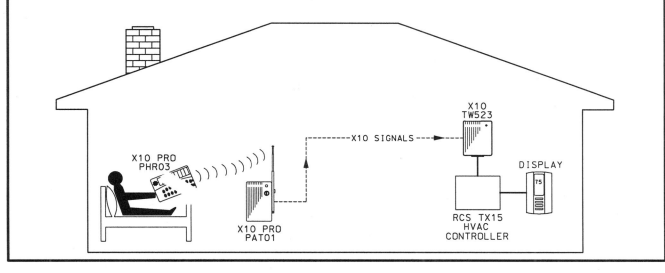

SYSTEM FEATURE 65
CALL HOME TO OPEN GARAGE BECAUSE DAUGHTER FORGOT HER KEY

A parent is at work and receives a phone call from the daughter at the neighbor's home. The child says she forgot her house key and can't get in the house. The parent tells the daughter to wait in front of the house for a moment. The parent hangs up and calls home. The Telephone Controller answers and prompts the parent to enter a password to access the system. The parent then dials *427. Symbol (*) = ON and button numbers 4-2-7 have letters **G-A-R** = garage on the phone buttons, so the parent does not need to memorize the code for each load. The Telephone Controller sends these commands to the TW523 Interface Module that converts Telephone Controller commands to X10 signals. This closes plug-in low voltage Receiver switch 6337 that opens the garage door. Set the 6337 to momentary closure, relay only.

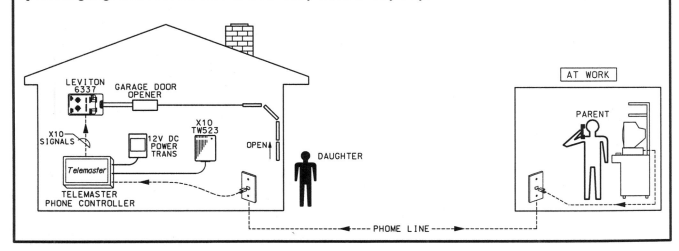

SYSTEM FEATURE 66
EASILY AUTOMATE A LIGHT WHEN THERE IS NO WALL SWITCH

An easy method of automating a light that does not have a plug-in cord and/or has a pull chain used for manual control, is to use a screw-in Receiver switch PSM04. Simply remove the light bulb, screw the Receiver switch into the existing fixture socket and set the address using a electronic means of programming. This is performed by transmitting the desired address three consecutive times using any type of X10 Transmitter.

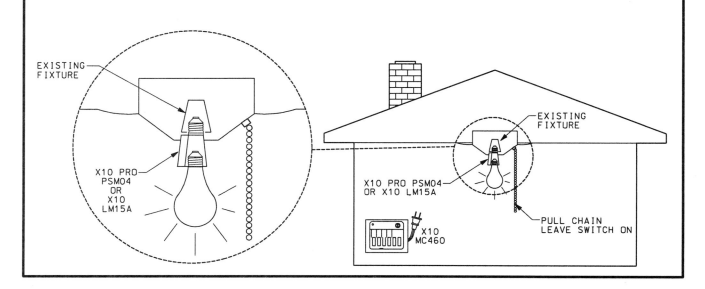

SYSTEM FEATURE 67
COMPUTER NETWORKING AND BROADBAND INTERNET

An Ethernet network is a transportation method of carrying groups of data between computers, peripherals and the Internet. A shared network allows users to share programs between computers on the network. Users can also back-up files to a different network computer. Documents can be printed from any network computer to a single system printer. Documents can be scanned and saved to any network computer and more than one computer can access the Internet at the same time. An Ethernet network consists of the five following elements: The cable that conveys data between computers, a network Interface card for each computer, an Ethernet frame, a modem and a Router used for Broadband Internet service. The Router is the device that actually groups the computers together at a central location using Category 5, 4 UTP cable.

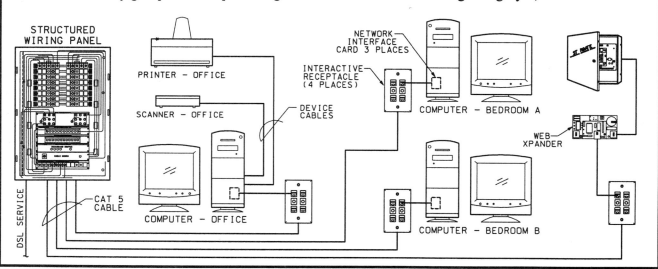

SYSTEM FEATURE 68
WIRELESS OPEN DOOR ANNOUNCER

An easy method of alerting a person that an individual is entering the home or business is to use a wireless Door Opening Announcer. When the Door Announcer RF Sensor/Transmitter detects door movement, it will transmit RF signals to the Door Announcer Receiver. When the Door Announcer Receiver receives these signals, it will activate an audible response by the door announcer. This system is especially useful in convenience stores and liquor stores because the employees may be stocking merchandise at the time and need to be alerted when customers enter.

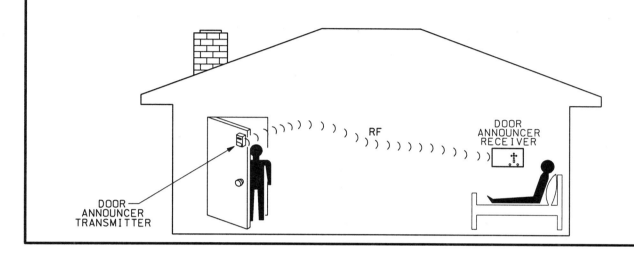

SYSTEM FEATURE 69
AUTOMATING HOME USING RCS X10 RELAY CONTROLLER PANEL

Using an RCS Relay panel is a good method of controlling certain types of electrical loads using low voltage contact closures. It avoids having to use a large number of X10 Universal low voltage Receiver switches. The relay panel offers two independent sets of contacts, so ON and OFF X10 signals can close or open contacts. A homeowner can simply transmit X10 commands from a 16-button tabletop Transmitter 6320 that will send X10 signals to Interface module PSC05. This device translates communications to operate the relay panel. This panel can control sprinkler systems, pool valves, pool pumps, pool heaters, garage doors, property access gates, automated thermostats, the Watercop leak detection system and many other electrical devices.

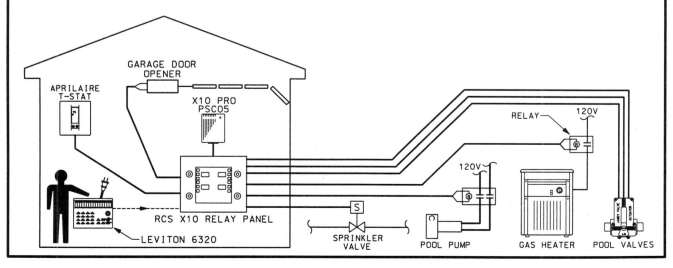

SYSTEM FEATURE 70
THE GOOD MORNING MODE

The Good Morning Mode can be automatically activated, for instance, at 6:00 AM Monday through Friday or by manually initiating an X10 Transmitting device when desired. This mode will brighten the bedroom lights, bathroom lights, hall lights and kitchen lights slowly over time to simulate sunrise. It will turn ON the coffee pot, turn ON the 'under the counter TV' for the morning news, disarm the security system, slowly open the drapes over time, turn ON the water heater, open the WaterCop leak detection system shutoff valve, adjust the air conditioning temperature set-points, turn on some mellow music and any other control functions that fit the homeowner's lifestyle.

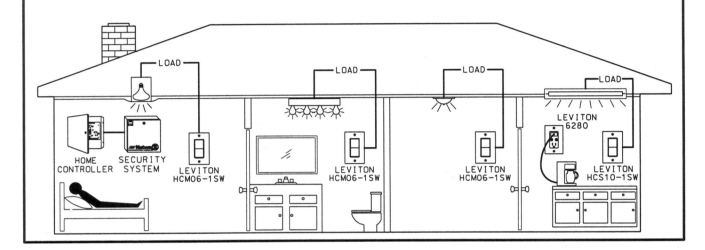

SYSTEM FEATURE 71
AUTOMATED ATTIC FAN

Attic ventilation fan thermostats inherently fail or are inaccurate. To remedy this problem, the homeowner can easily install a Slimline mechanical temperature sensor that has two N.O. contacts. Most attics have a light switch and/or power receptacle. If only a light switch is available, install a single gang electrical box and receptacle next to the light switch enclosure to plug-in Transmitter 6330. The temperature sensor and Transmitter 6330 are installed in the attic and are wired as shown. When the temperature in the attic, for instance, reaches 100 degrees F as set on the temperature sensor, the N.O. contacts in the sensor will close and Transmitter 6330 will transmit X10-ON signals to Receiver switch HCS10 to turn the fan ON. When the temperature drops below 98 degrees F, the contacts will open and Transmitter 6330 will transmit X10-OFF signals to Receiver switch HCS10 to turn the fan OFF.

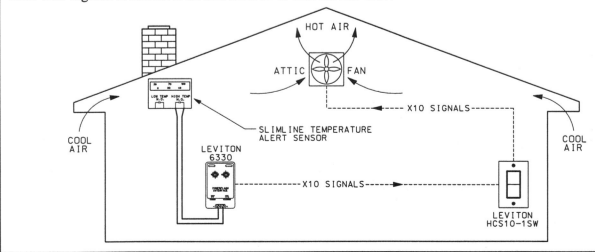

SYSTEM FEATURE 72
AUTOMATED LANDSCAPE WATER FOUNTAIN

An automated water fountain is normally controlled ON and OFF based on a time schedule similar to how a pool pump is controlled. In this example the pump is controlled ON at 8:00 AM each day and OFF at 7:00 PM. The Home Controller has an internal time clock, so it knows exactly when to control any electrical load that is on a time schedule. At 8:00 AM the Home Controller closes a set of low voltage Relay Output contacts that close a motor start relay to start the 240V pump. At 7:00 PM the Home Controller opens the Relay Out contacts to open the starter relay and stop the pump.

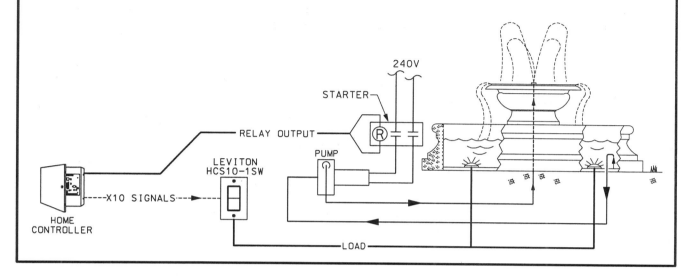

SYSTEM FEATURE 73
POWERFLASH MODULE SENSES ALARM CONDITION & FLASHES LIGHTS

The Burglar Alarm Interface 6330 is a device used to control electrical loads based on various conditions. It is generally used to turn ON lights or flash the lights when it senses either a dry contact closure or low voltage (6 – 18 volts AC, DC). In the example shown below, a plug-in Burglar Alarm Interface 6330 is wired to an auxiliary output and the auxiliary power terminals. To sense a voltage in this case the slide switch located on the face of the 6330 needs to be moved to 'Input A'. To simply turn the lights ON, the other slide switch must be in Mode 1 or 3. To flash the lights, Mode 2 is necessary. When the security system is in an alarm condition, the auxiliary output is programmed to close. The low voltage in this circuit is sensed by the 6330, which transmits X10 signals to control Receiver switches 2384 and PLM03.

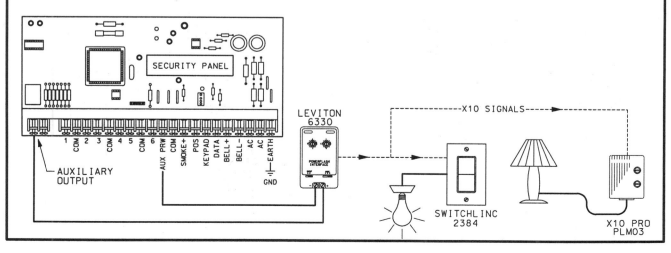

SYSTEM FEATURE 74
PROTECT FREEZER FOOD FROM GETTING SPOILED

Sometimes a home has a stand-alone freezer located in a large kitchen, inside the laundry room or in the garage. These locations generally have GFI power receptacles required by building codes. If the GFI receptacle trips due to a lightning strike, power surge, brown out, etc., all the receptacles wired on the GFI circuit will have power removed. When a freezer is plugged into one of these receptacles, there is the potential for the GFI to trip without the owner knowing it for days. To solve this problem the homeowner could run a long extension cord to a receptacle that is not on a GFI circuit or install the system shown below. If the GFI is tripped, the power out sensor will sense the lack of 120V and close a set of internal N.O. low voltage contacts that are wired to a PF284 Transmitter. This device will then send X10 signals to plug-in siren PH508 located inside the home to alert the homeowner immediately.

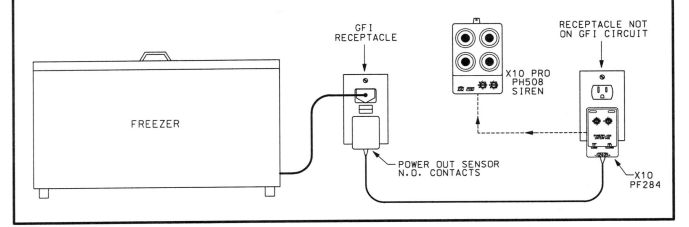

SYSTEM FEATURE 75
A HARDWIRED SECURITY SYSTEM

In the system shown below, a typical hardwired security system is illustrated. When the security system has been armed and the exit delay period has expired, the system has the potential to alarm. If a burglar enters the front door or garage door the system will not alarm immediately because of a delay programmed into the system to allow the homeowner to disarm the system on arrival from the keypad. If a window sensor, motion sensor or smoke sensor is tripped, the system will alarm immediately. The alarm will sound the sirens, flash the lights, turn ON the strobe light, notify the monitoring company and even notify the owner by phone or E-mail. The strobe light alerts the homeowner upon arrival that the burglar may still be in the home and is also used to help the authorities find the home easier.

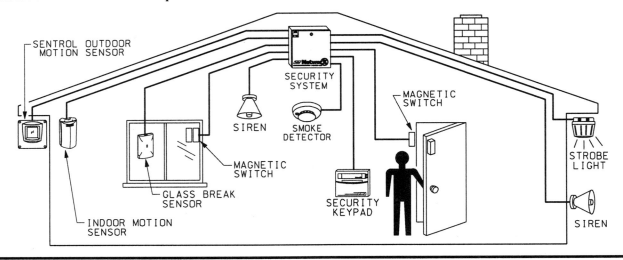

SYSTEM FEATURE 76
WHEN GARAGE IS OPENED AFTER SUNSET, GARAGE LIGHTS TURN ON

When the garage door is opened after sunset by using the garage door manual keypad, handheld remote, command from the Home Controller, or by hand, the lights in the garage will automatically turn ON. When the door opens the standard N.C. magnetic switch will open and the OMNI II controller will detect this condition. When this occurs, the OMNI II transmits X10-ON signals to Receiver switch HCS10 that turns the garage lights ON. When the door is closed, the N.C. magnetic switch will close, which is sensed by OMNI II. This tells the OMNI to transmit X10-OFF signals to Receiver switch HCS10 that turns the lights OFF. This function will occur only when it is after sunset and before sunrise.

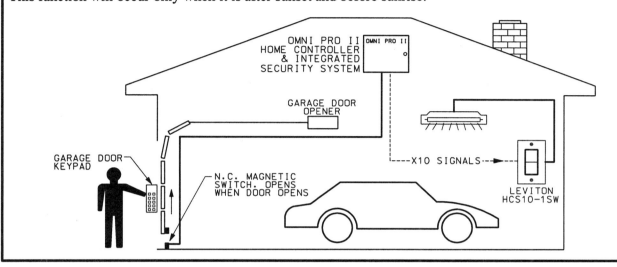

SYSTEM FEATURE 77
BE ALERTED WHEN AIR CONDITIONING FILTER IS DIRTY

This feature provides the homeowner with a reminder that the air conditioning filter needs to be changed. This reminder is not based on the amount of time that has lapse since the last time the filter was replaced. It is initiated based on the pressure difference across the filter. When the filter is clean the pressure difference across the filter is low. When it is dirty the pressure differential is high. We can actually measure the pressure difference by installing a differential pressure switch across the filter in the air handler. When the filter is dirty the switch will trip and will send a Digital Input to the Home Controller. This will tell the Home Controller to provide a voice response over a speaker or Whole House audio system as follows: "AC filter need changing".

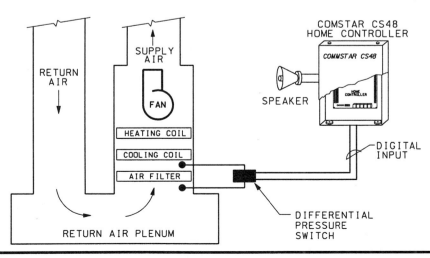

SYSTEM FEATURE 78
LEAST EXPENSIVE MEANS OF AUTOMATING LIGHTS

An easy and quick method of automating a few lights in the home is to install screw in motion activated occupancy sensors. Another method is to replace a light switch with an in-wall occupancy sensor as shown below. Areas of the home where occupants are present for a short period of time lend themselves well for this application. These areas may include hallways, pantries, closets, laundry rooms, etc. In pantries and in closets, it is best to install the wired in occupancy sensor in the ceiling. This means the occupancy sensor/switch would be wired between the existing wall switch and the light fixture. This configuration will operate properly by always leaving the exiting wall switch in the ON position.

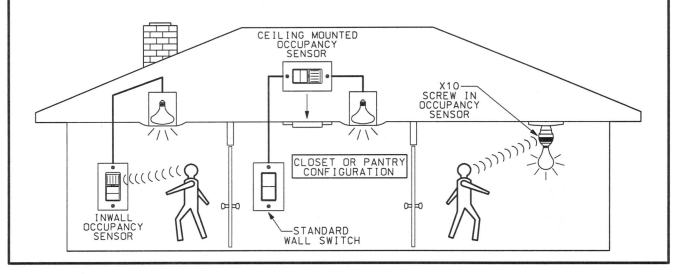

SYSTEM FEATURE 79
AUTOMATICALLY TURN OFF AIR CONDITIONING WHEN A WINDOW OR DOOR IS OPENED

In this feature, the air conditioning system is turned OFF automatically when any window or door is left open for more than 30 seconds. The system operates as follows: If an occupant opens a door or window, the associated N.C. magnetic switch will open, which notifies the security panel of this condition. The Omni II combination Home Controller/Security System programming includes the 30 second time delay between the moment a window or door opens and the command from the controller is sent to turn OFF the air conditioning system. The OMNI II will turn OFF the air conditioning system by selecting the OFF Mode as if it was manually selected at the thermostat.

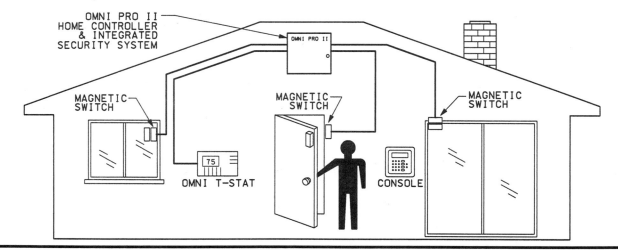

56

SYSTEM FEATURE 80
DISCOURAGE POTENTIAL BURGLARS BEFORE THEY BREAK IN

In this feature the family is on vacation and need some extra security. A 'would-be-burglar' approaches the home and is detected by the wireless motion detector DM10A. The motion detector transmits RF signals that are received by the plug-in Electronic Watchdog. When this occurs the Watchdog is activated and provides an audible barking dog response. After a short delay, the Watchdog transmits X10-ON signals to both Receiver switches to turn the lights ON. The time delay before it turns on the lights is designed to appear as though someone in the home is responding to the dog's actions.

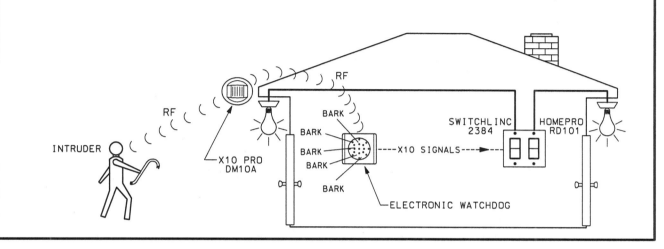

SYSTEM FEATURE 81
ALL-IN-ONE HOME AUTOMATION AND SECURITY SYSTEM CONTROLLER

This system is an all in one integrated Home Controller and Security System. This expands the power of the home automation system because it allows the home control portion of the system to monitor the security system sensors, alarm condition, arm and disarm states as well as others. Changing states of the security system can be used to initiate home control functions. The OMNI PRO II system operates by performing modes that include: The Good Night Mode, Leaving Home Mode, Arriving Home Mode, Good Morning Mode, etc. These modes control lighting, air conditioning, arm/disarm functions, etc. Modes can be activated based on date and time of day, sunrise and sunset times, X10 signals, Digital Inputs, Analog Inputs, telephone commands or commands made over the Internet. Programming can be performed using a PC or from the OMNI interface console.

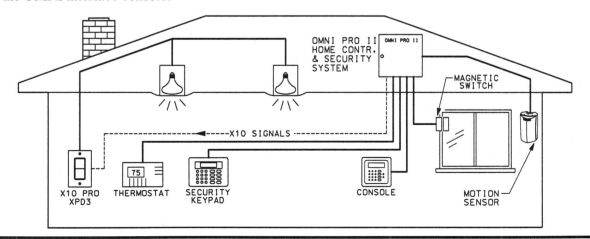

57

SYSTEM FEATURE 82
INTEGRATED HOME CONTROL SYSTEM AND SECURITY SYSTEM

Another integrated system consists of an RS-232 communication connection between the *Stargate* or *CommStar* Home Controller and the CADDX NX8-E security panel. This allows the Home Controller to read what state the security system is in at any time and the state of each individual sensor. This allows the Home Controller to initiate home control functions based on this information. The Home Controller can also arm and disarm the security system, bypass security zones, activate the medical panic, police panic, fire panic as well as other security modes and functions. See the **Latest Technology In Automated Home Control** for detailed information on how to Design Systems and integrate these components.

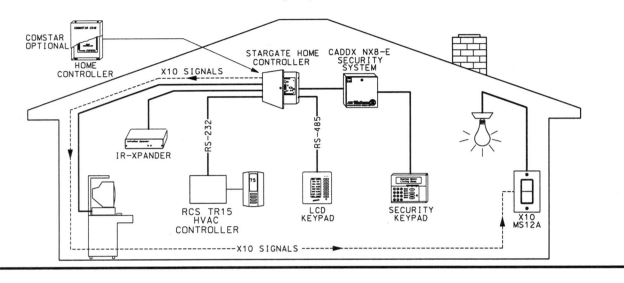

SYSTEM FEATURE 83
WHEN PHONE IS ANSWERED OR DOOR BELL RINGS A/V VOLUME IS LOWERED

This feature allows an occupant that answers the phone an opportunity to quickly carry on a phone conversation without having to walk over to the A/V equipment to manually lower the volume. When the phone is answered (off-hook) the Home Controller detects this condition and has the IR-Xpander send the proper IR signals to the audio receiver to lower the volume. If someone rings the doorbell, the Home Controller will receive a Digital Input from the doorbell unit. This is another condition that allows the IR-Xpander to send volume adjustment commands. When the phone conversation is over and the occupant hangs the phone up (On-hook) the volume returns to it previous level.

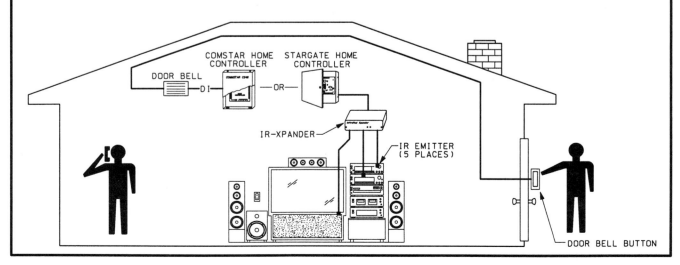

SYSTEM FEATURE 84
AUTOMATE YOUR HOME USING YOUR PERSONAL COMPUTER

For beginners that want to control their home using their PC, and will be content with limited control capability compared to other home automation controllers, the active home computer interface is a good choice. The active home software for Windows is used to develop a schedule that controls lights and appliances at different times of day. Once this is complete the schedule is downloaded to the computer interface that plugs into a standard power receptacle. The computer interface remembers the schedule and transmits X10 signals over the power lines to various Receiver switches to perform the end functions.

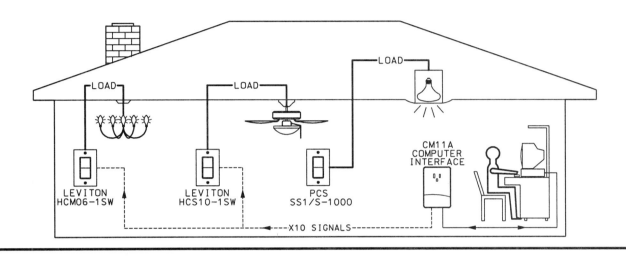

SYSTEM FEATURE 85
WATER DAMAGE PREVENTION SYSTEM FOR THE LAUNDRY ROOM

Most water leaks in the home occur in the laundry room when a water hose serving the clothes washer bursts. The system shown below consists of shutoff valves mounted to the hot and cold water pipes. The standard water hoses are then connected to the shutoff valves. The control unit is mounted to a wall and the control wires are connected to the shutoff valves. The water sensor is positioned on the floor as shown. If a water leak occurs in the room, the water sensor will detect the leak and notify the control unit of this condition. The control unit will then close both shutoff valves to avoid water damage and will also sound the alarm to alert the occupants.

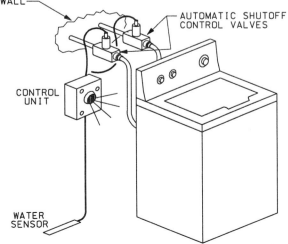

SYSTEM FEATURE 86
ARRIVING HOME MODE INITIATED AT THE FRONT DOOR

There are two different Arriving Home Modes associated with a home automation system. One is initiated when arriving home by car and the other is initiated when arriving home through the front door. The Arriving Home Mode is initiated at the front door by using a push button keychain remote that sends RF signals to Transceiver PAT01. After receiving these signals, the Transceiver will transmit X10 signals over the power lines to the Home Controller. The Home Controller will then transmit X10 signals to the appropriate Receiver switches to turn ON the exterior lights and one light in each room if it is after sunset for safety purposes. The heating and cooling temperature set-points are reset, draperies are opened, music is turned ON, the water heater is turned ON, the security system is disarmed and any other control function that the homeowner would like to include to suite his lifestyle.

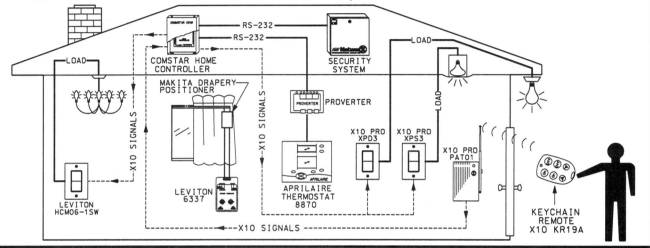

SYSTEM FEATURE 87
REMOTELY CONTROL BOATHOUSE LIGHTS UPON ARRIVAL

In this feature the boat owner needs to have sufficient lighting when approaching the boathouse after sunset. Lighting is initiated by pushing a button on keychain remote KR19A. The remote sends out RF signals that are received by Transceiver PAT01. The Transceiver then transmits X10 signals over the power lines and both 6291 Receiver switches respond by turning ON interior and exterior boathouse lights. This mode can also notify the spouse in the home that the husband has arrived by sounding a chime or by a prerecorded message broadcast over the whole house audio system. Once the boat is docked and secured and the husband has entered the home, he can push a wall Transmitter button to turn OFF the boathouse lighting and the walkway lighting that leads up to the home.

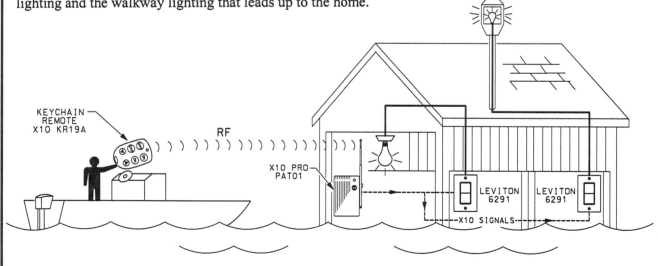

SYSTEM FEATURE 88
CONTROL YOUR HOME WITH VOICE COMMANDS

This is an interesting feature that controls the home by simple voice commands using continuous voice recognition. No programming is required. Only easy wizard driven menus are used. By speaking into an open microphone connected to the PC, or by picking up any phone and pressing the appropriate buttons, lighting, air conditioning, sprinkler system, audio/video equipment and any other electrical device can be controlled. Electrical devices can also be controlled from anywhere in the world by calling the home and entering an access code before pressing the appropriate buttons to control specific electrical devices. HAL can also be asked to read the users e-mail messages. HAL also announces who is calling on the phone by placing caller ID on the TV screen or PC monitor. Refer to the HAL web site for additional features.

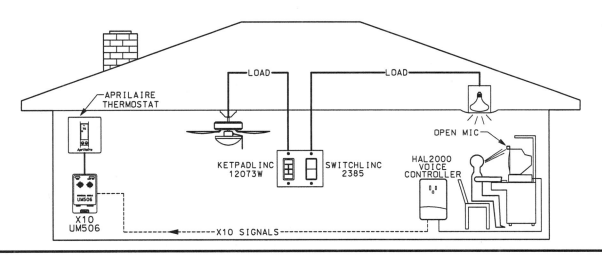

SYSTEM FEATURE 89
IF THE CARBON MONOXIDE LEVEL IS HIGH, OPEN GARAGE DOOR

This feature protects individuals from high carbon monoxide levels produced by internal combustion engines. If the carbon monoxide level gets too high in the garage, the Home Controller will read the carbon monoxide level from the sensor through an Analog Input or Digital Input. The Home Controller will then open the garage by momentarily closing a Relay Output. It will also transmit X10-ON signals over the power lines to Receiver switch HCS10 to turn the garage lights ON and alert the occupants in the home by activating the security system alarm or independent alarm.

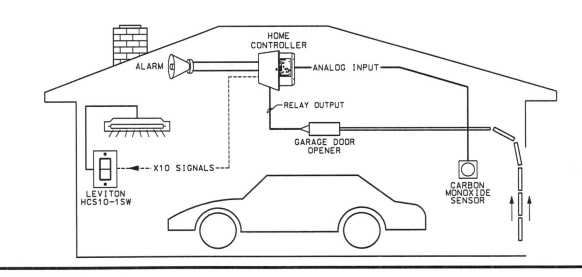

SYSTEM FEATURE 90
CHECK ON THE KIDS IN THE POOL AREA

This system feature allows parents to monitor the kids in the pool area while making lunch. The hardwired motion detector located on the pool patio is used to detect the children in the pool area. These conductors are wired to a Digital Input on the Home Controller. When the children are detected, the Home Controller is able to read this condition. The Home Controller will then close a Relay Output to turn ON the CCTV camera on the patio. At the same time the Home Controller will communicate to the IR-Xpander. The IR-Xpander will then send the appropriate IR signals to the Kitchen TV to automatically turn it ON and select the proper channel, so the parent can view the children's activities. When the children get out of hand or it is time for lunch, the parent can communicate with them by using the home's intercom system.

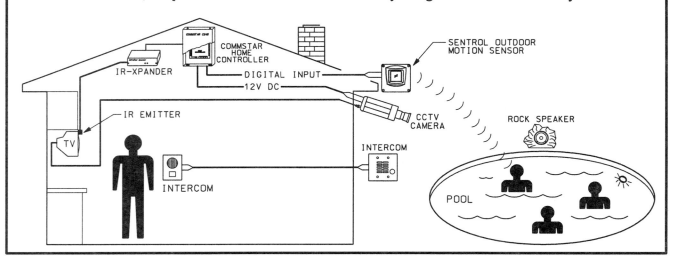

SYSTEM FEATURE 91
AUTOMATIC NOTIFICATION THAT THE POOL FILTER IS DIRTY

This feature provides the homeowner with a voice response over the whole house audio system that the pool filter needs cleaning. This system consists of a differential pressure switch that measures the pressures across the filter. A tube is connected to the pool piping on each side of the filter. The other ends of the tubes are connected to the differential pressure switch to allow water pressure monitoring. As the filter gets dirty, it becomes more difficult for the pump to flow water through it, which increases the pressure difference across the filter. When the differential get too high, the switch will close and the Digital Input is read by the Home Controller. The Home Controller will then initiate a voice response that states the following: "Pool filter needs cleaning".

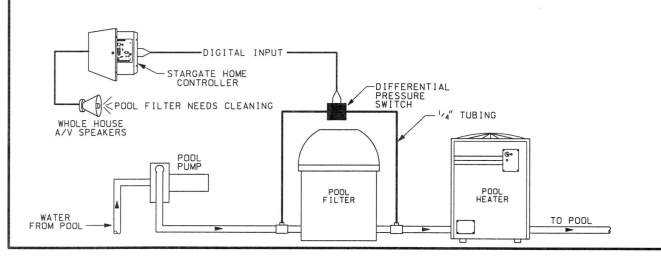

SYSTEM FEATURE 92
WHOLE HOUSE AUDIO/VIDEO SYSTEM

The whole house audio system provides music to any room in the home. The system consists of in-wall speakers, ceiling speakers, patio surface mounted speakers and rock speakers. Sixteen gauge speaker wire is pulled during new construction from the audio equipment location to each speaker in the system. Category 5 cable is also pulled to each wall keypad location. Music selections can be made in each room from the wall keypad, so the user does not need to walk to the audio equipment to make selections. The conductors are connected to a NUVO Kustom 6, 6 room, 6 audio source whole house audio amplifier. This device provides the capability of listening to a radio station in one room, a CD in another room and satellite audio in the family room. See the back panel of this device shown below.

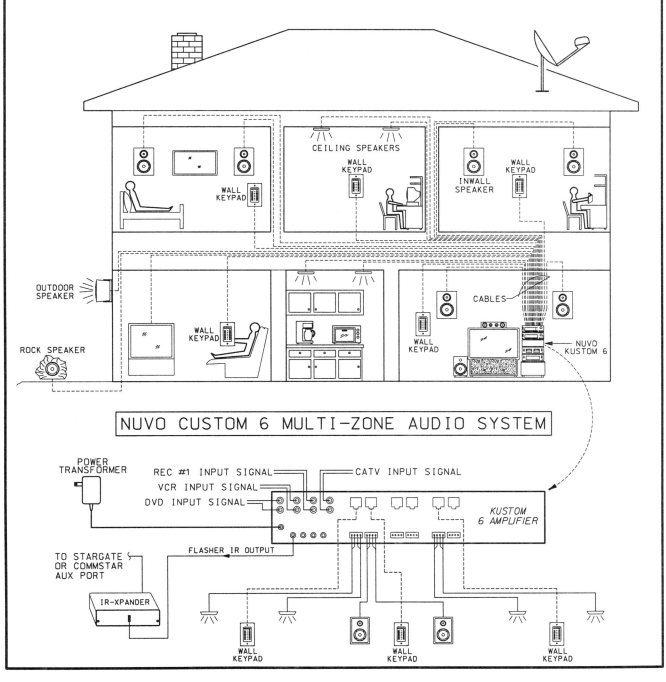

SYSTEM FEATURE 93
SAVE ENERGY WITH AUTOMATED CONTROL OF THE HOME HOT WATER CIRCULATION SYSTEM

This system circulates hot water continuously throughout the home, so when hot water is needed at any location, it is available immediately. The circulation pump is small when it comes to pumps; however, it still uses needless energy when the occupants are away from the home or at night. This home control feature saves energy by circulating hot water only during times when hot water may be needed. This feature is normally one of many control functions performed by the Leaving Home Mode, Vacation Mode and Good Night Mode because these are times when instant hot water is not necessary. The circulation pump is turned back ON when the Arriving Home Mode or Good Morning Mode are activated. Modes are initiated either automatically or remotely from a Transmitter that sends X10 signals to the Home Controller. The Home Controller will then perform all mode functions that include X10 signal transmissions to turn ON or OFF Receiver receptacle 6280 that powers the circulation pump.

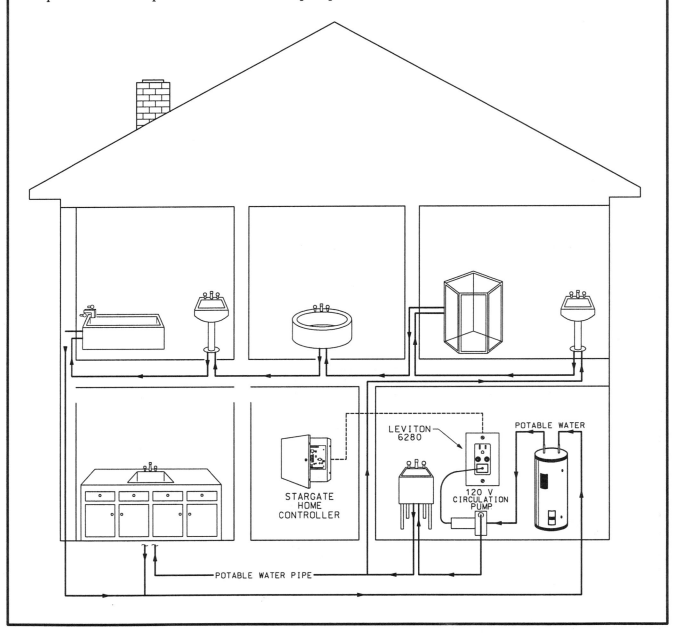

SYSTEM FEATURE 94
EARLY DETECTION OF AN INTRUDER ON THE PROPERTY

This feature provides the homeowner with early indication that someone has penetrated the gated perimeter and is potentially moving towards the house. The intruder is detected by dual beam photoelectric sensors that project beams across the property. When someone breaks the beam the sensor opens an internal switch and the Security System along with the Home Controller reads this condition. This notifies the system to activate the alarm, notify the monitoring service, turn on exterior lights, turn on CCTV cameras and video viewing equipment and send prerecorded voice response messages played over the outdoor speakers. It may also alert the bodyguards of the intrusion or automatically release the dogs from their pens.

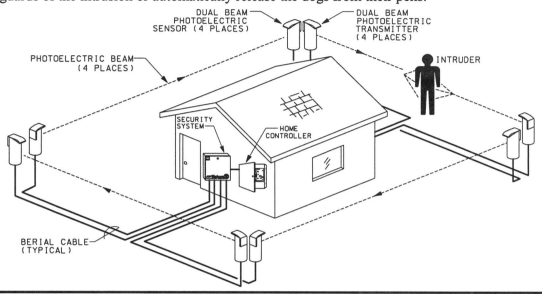

SYSTEM FEATURE 95
THE ENTERTAINMENT MODE

The Entertainment Mode is initiated in this example by using hand-held remote UR19A. This device sends IR signals to the in-wall IR receiver as shown. The IR Input is carrier by the conductors to the IR-Xpander, which is connected to the Home Controller. When the Home Controller reads these signals, it will transmit X10 signals over the power lines to Receiver switch HCMO6-1SW to dim the lights to 20% bright. X10 signals are also sent to Receiver switch 2380 to turn OFF perimeter lighting. X10 signals will also turn OFF the wall receptacle and then turn it back ON to close the draperies. The IR-Xpander sends IR signals to the audio/video equipment to turn ON the TV, audio receiver, NUVO audio amplifier, DVD player and other A/V equipment automatically.

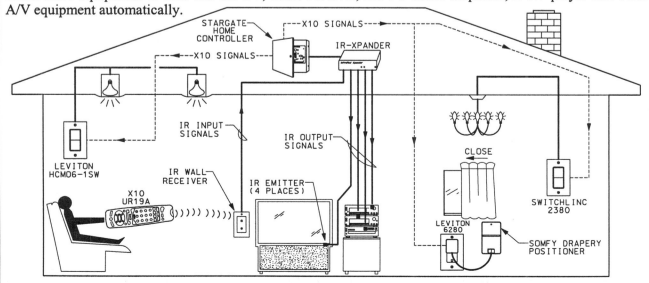

SYSTEM FEATURE 96
AUTOMATIC ACTIVATION OF THE ARRIVING HOME MODE

This feature provides automatic initiation of the Arriving Home Mode only when an occupant's vehicle enters the driveway. This is because only the family vehicles have a transponder mounted to the vehicle's chassis. When the vehicle drives over the control grid installed in the concrete driveway, the transponder is sensed and is read by the driveway grid control unit. The control unit will then close a set of contacts that sends a Digital Input to the Home Controller, which will in turn activated the Arriving Home Mode. Refer to this mode in Feature 7 and 8.

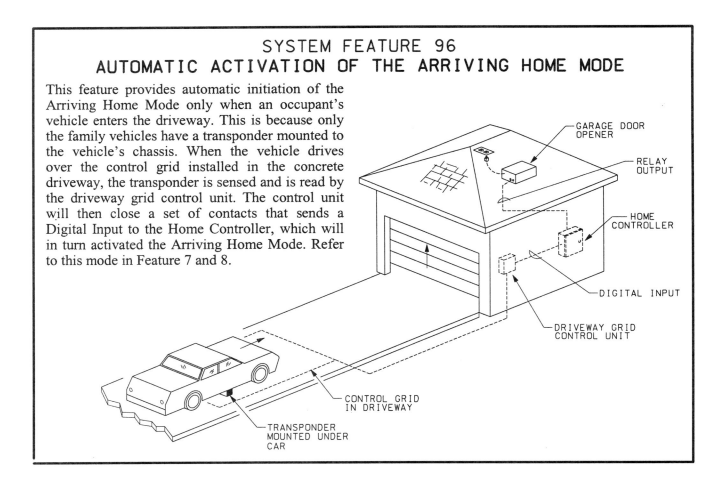

SYSTEM FEATURE 97
CAN'T REMEMBER IF YOU CLOSED THE GARAGE DOOR?

The homeowner leaves for work and is thinking about what needs to be accomplished for the day. She is two miles down the road and the question pops into her mind; did I close the garage door? She is already late for work and hates to return home, so she calls home on her cell phone. When the phone is answered by the Telephone Controller, she is prompted to enter a password so she pushes a series of buttons on the phone to access the system. Once she is into the system, she pushes buttons #43. The symbol # equals a **close** command, button 4 also has the letter **G** on it for '**garage**' and button 3 also has the letter **D** on it for '**door**'. The Telephone Controller sends the X10 commands to Receiver switch 6337 that is wired to the N.O. magnetic style security switch. If the door is in the open position, the magnetic switch is closed and the door will close when Receiver switch 6637 closes. If the door is already closed, the magnetic switch will be open and the door will not move when Receiver switch 6637 is closed.

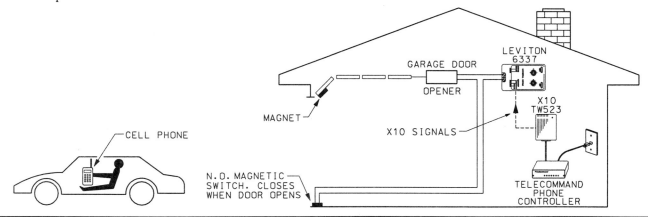

SYSTEM FEATURE 98
REPLACE EXISTING SWITCH WITH A TRANSMITTER

One of the biggest hassles when installing a wall Transmitter is having to add or replace an existing switch box with an extra gang for the Transmitter. One way to avoid this hassle is to install the Receiver switch inside the light fixture and use the existing switch gang for the Transmitter. This is illustrated below. An even better method is to install a KeypadLinc, which is basically a combination Receiver switch and push button Transmitter all in one. This means that all an installer needs to do is remove the existing mechanical wall switch and replace it with the KeypadLinc, which will provide automated switching and dimming control of the light. It will also provide available buttons on the KeypadLinc to be used to control additional loads or to initiate home automation modes.

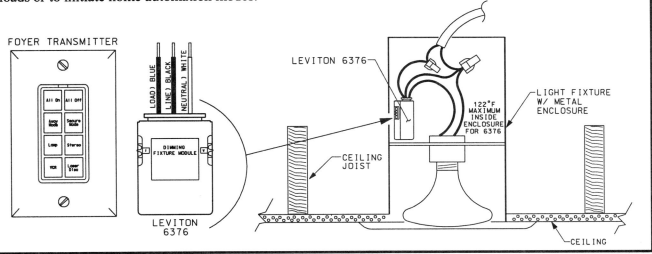

SYSTEM FEATURE 99
HOME ENERGY MANAGEMENT SYSTEM

One of the main features of a home automation system is energy management. When the occupants are not at home the heating and cooling temperature set-points are setback and the water heater is turned OFF to save energy. Some of the other electrical devices that are turned OFF to save energy are the lights, ceiling fans, audio/video equipment, domestic hot water circulation pump and any other electrical device that does not need to be ON while the occupants are away or at night. The pool pump and sprinkler system pump are both controlled on a time schedule to save energy, and running the dishwasher automatically at 2:00AM each morning can help to lower peak energy usage.

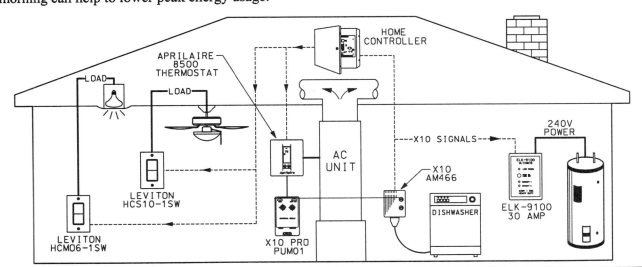

SYSTEM FEATURE 100
REMOTE CONTROL OF VIDEO SCREEN

The user can remotely position the video screen by using Universal Remote HCCUR, Receiver switch 6337 and Transceiver PAT01. To position the screen for viewing or rolled up to get it out of the way, the Receiver switch needs to be opened first and then closed. To perform this function, RF-OFF signals and then RF-ON signals are transmitted from the Universal Remote to the plug-in Transceiver. The Transceiver then transmits X10-OFF signals and then X10-ON signals over the power lines to the plug-in low voltage Receiver switch 6337. When this switch opens and then closes, the screen is rolled down and is stopped by its own internal limit switch. To roll the screen up, the user must again turn OFF the Receiver switch and then turn it back ON. Please refer to Feature 91 for an alternate method of controlling the projector screen.

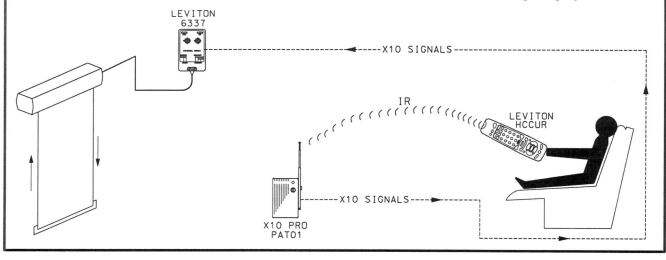

SYSTEM FEATURE 101
AN OPTIONAL METHOD OF CONTROLLING VIDEO SCREEN

An optional method of remotely controlling the video screen is shown below. Audio receivers have an AC power receptacle that turns ON when the audio receiver is turned ON with an IR remote or by pushing the audio receiver's ON button. It is generally used to turn on other A/V equipment when the audio receiver is turned ON. By plugging in a low voltage transformer into this receptacle and wiring it to plug-in Burglar Alarm Interface 6330, the video screen can be remotely rolled down. Each time the audio receiver is turned ON, the Burglar alarm interface will sense the low voltage from the transformer and transmit X10-ON signals to the low voltage Receiver switch to reposition the screen. When the audio receiver is turned OFF, the 6337 shown in Feature 100 is turned OFF. For this reason it does not need an initial OFF command the next time the audio receiver is turned ON.

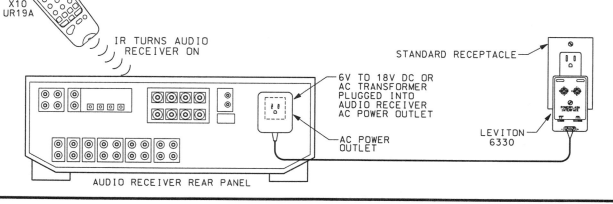

SYSTEM FEATURE 102
THE PARTY MODE

The Party Mode basically adjusts the lighting in the home to the appropriate brightness levels based on the party activities. It also turns on exterior lighting to provide sufficient light to greet guests. The air conditioning set-points are generally adjusted to provide the guests with a more comfortable environment than normal. Ceiling fans in certain rooms are turned ON to supplement cooling. The fresh air damper is generally opened to compensate for higher CO_2 levels due to a greater number of people in the home. The Spa Mode can also be initiated as one of the many functions provided by the Party Mode.

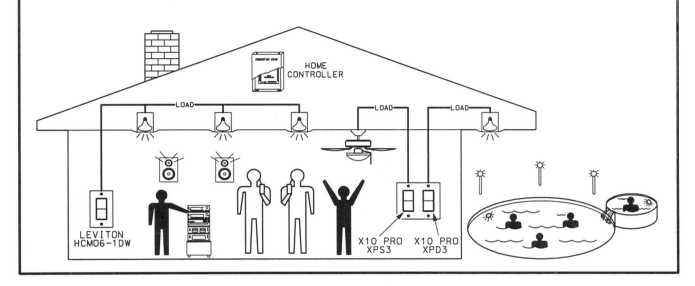

SYSTEM FEATURE 103
AUTOMATING A CEILING FAN WHEN THERE IS NO WALL SWITCH

In many older homes the ceiling fans with or without light-kits were installed without wall switches to control them. Without automation techniques, the only means of controlling this type of fan and or light fixture is with the existing pull chains. To automate this type of ceiling fan, a Receiver switch needs to be installed somewhere because every electrical load needs a Receiver switch. In this case, the best option is to install a fixture Receiver switch inside the escutcheon cover as shown. There will generally not be sufficient space to install another fixture Receiver switch for the light-kit. One option is to wire the fan and light together so when the fan is remotely controlled ON the light will also turn ON. If this is not acceptable, then control the light manually as needed.

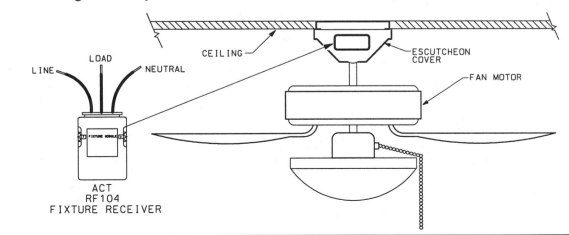

SYSTEM FEATURE 104
AUTOMATED SUMP PUMP

This feature provides a means of pumping water out of the basement in case of flooding due to rain or a water leak in the home. If flooding should occur, the N.O. float switch will raise and close its internal switch. This closure will be sensed by the PF284 Transmitter that will send X10-ON signals to Receiver switch 6291 to turn the sump pump ON. When the water level lowers to an acceptable level, the float switch will open and the PF284 will transmit X10-OFF signals to turn the pump OFF.

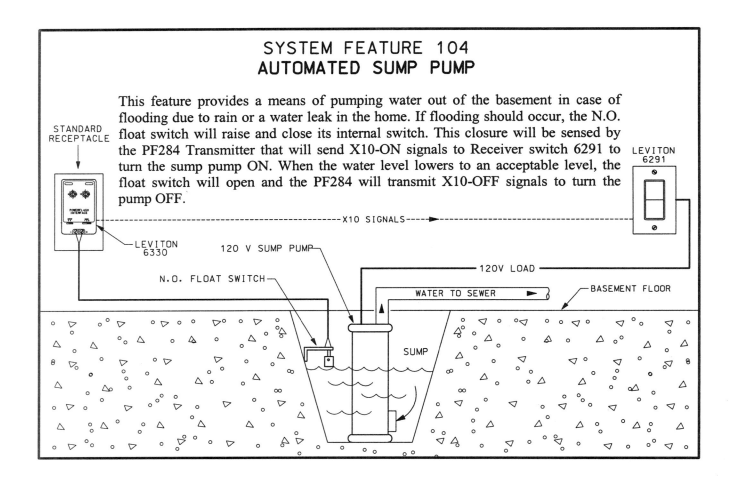

SYSTEM FEATURE 105
WHOLE HOUSE AUDIO SYSTEM PROVIDES
MESSAGES TO FAMILY MEMBERS

This feature is very useful to remind family members of important events using voice responses. These responses are initiated by the Home Controller and are broadcast over the whole house audio system. Voice responses may include the following: "Dads birthday soon", "someone on property", "laundry room leak", "garage door open", "clean AC filter", take out garbage". Specific voice responses can also be initiated by selecting assigned buttons on Universal Remote UR19A. The Home Controller will make sure that the IR-Xpander maintains the whole house receiver amplifier ON to broadcast voice responses when necessary. Low priority voice responses will activate only during awake hours; however, if the voice response is related to safety or security it will be broadcast at any hour.

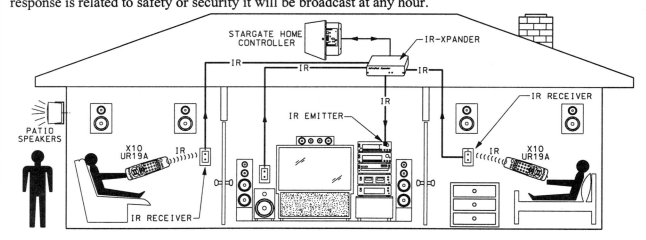

SYSTEM FEATURE 106
THE ECONOMIZER MODE

The following description and sequence of operation will explain the Economizer Mode. If the home requires cooling and the outdoor temperature sensor and humidity sensor readings are less than the interior set-points, the Home Controller will read these conditions and open the outside air damper to condition the home economically. When the outside air conditions are no longer acceptable and the home is still calling for cooling, the outside air damper will be controlled closed and the air conditioning system will operate normally. The Economizer Mode can also be used for heating under the right circumstances.

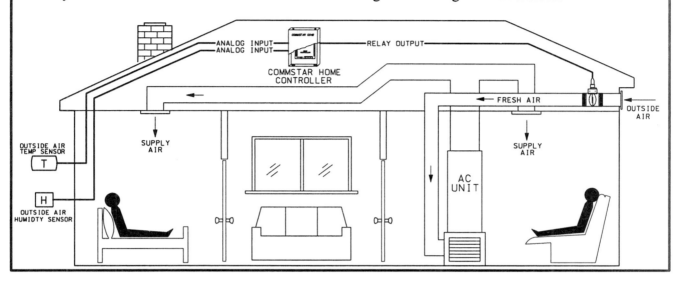

SYSTEM FEATURE 107
AUTOMATICALLY CLOSE WINDOW COVERINGS WHEN IT IS HOT OR COLD OUTSIDE TO SAVE ENERGY

Another Energy Management feature of a home automation system is the method of increasing the resistance value at the windows to decrease the rate of heat being transferred either into or out of the home. This resistance value called R-value, can be increased by closing the window coverings when the outside reaches high or low temperatures. In the example shown below, an outside air temperature sensor is installed. When the temperature reaches 95 degrees F, the Home Controller reads this condition and closes a Relay Output to control the Makita drapery positioner closed. When the outside air temperature is less than 55 degrees F, the drapes or other type of window covering is closed to keep the heat in.

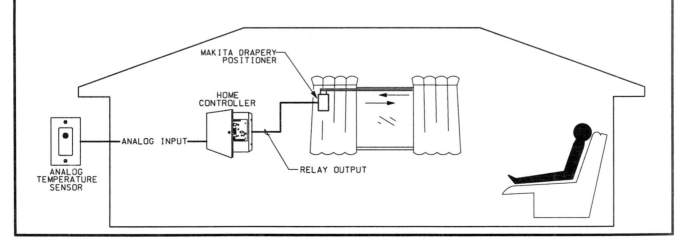

SYSTEM FEATURE 108
THE GOOD NIGHT MODE

The Good Night Mode can be activated by a time schedule or initiated remotely by using a transmitting device. In the example shown below, an occupant uses Universal Remote PUR08 to send RF signals to Transceiver PAT01. The Transceiver then sends X10 signals to the Home Controller to trigger the mode. This mode turns OFF select lighting, ceiling fans, changes the heating and cooling set-points, closes the drapes, arms the security system, checks the garage door closed, turns OFF the water heater, and turns OFF power receptacles used by appliances with heating elements. This mode also turns on the appropriate lighting required to walk to the bedrooms and bathrooms to get ready for bed.

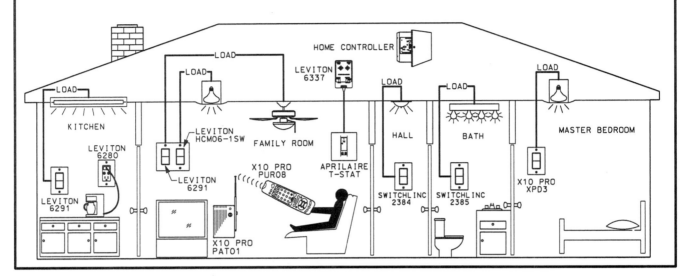

SYSTEM FEATURE 109
THE IN BED MODE

After the Good Night Mode is activated and the occupants have finished getting ready for bed and are now in bed, the 'In Bed Mode' can be initiated. The 'In Bed Mode' is initiated in this example by using hand-held remote PUR08. This device sends RF signals that are received by Transceiver PAT01. The Transceiver then sends X10 signals over the power lines to turn OFF the lights that were turned ON by the Good Night Mode to provide sufficient lighting to get ready for bed. Reference Feature 108 for the description of the Good Night Mode.

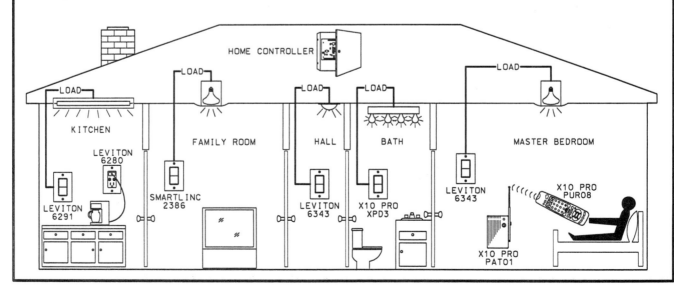

SYSTEM FEATURE 110
SNACK MODE IN THE MIDDLE OF THE NIGHT

The Snack Mode allows an occupant with sufficient lighting to get to the Kitchen and back to the Bedroom. The Bathroom Mode works in a similar fashion. When an occupant wants to get out of bed and go to the Kitchen for whatever reason, she would push a button on Transmitter TK184. The Transmitter will send X10 signals to the Home Controller to activate the mode. This mode will turn ON the Hallway, Dining Room, Family Room and Kitchen lights to 20% bright, so the lighting is not hard on the eyes. When the occupant returns to bed, she will push the mode OFF button to turn the lights OFF.

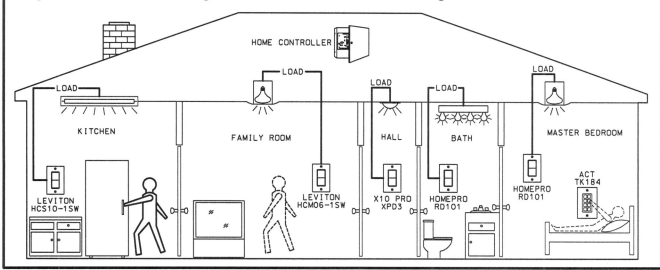

SYSTEM FEATURE 111
THE VACATION MODE

The Vacation Mode changes all electrical devices to a state that the homeowner wants them in while away on vacation. This mode turns OFF all lighting inside the home and turns ON exterior lighting if the mode is initiated after dark for exiting purposes. This mode will also close the drapes, turn OFF the ceiling fans and audio/video equipment, and shutoff the WaterCop valve. This mode will set-back the heating and cooling set-points and turn OFF the water heater to save energy. It will also automatically arm the security system and set the vacation programming Flag that will allow the Deterrent Mode to potential run if a would-be-burglar approach the home after dark. Refer to the Deterrent Mode in Feature 112. The Vacation Mode will also periodically turn on lights, open drapes and control other loads to make the home look lived in.

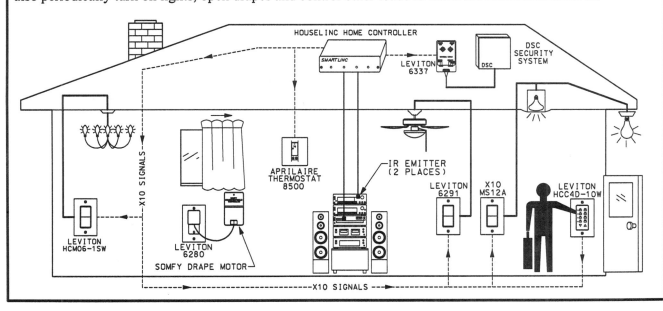

SYSTEM FEATURE 112: THE DETERRENT MODE

The Deterrent Mode can only run after the Leaving Home Mode or Vacation Mode has been activated. This mode is designed to control a variety of electrical loads when an intruder is detected in the yard. For instance, if an intruder approaches the home and a security light motion detector picks the individual up, lights in the home will turn ON and dim to a 60% brightness level and the drapes may partially open. The stereo or TV may also be turned ON only in the part of the house closest to the motion sensor. This mode is a great deterrent because if the burglar feels that people are at home, he will feel it is much easier to burglarize elsewhere.

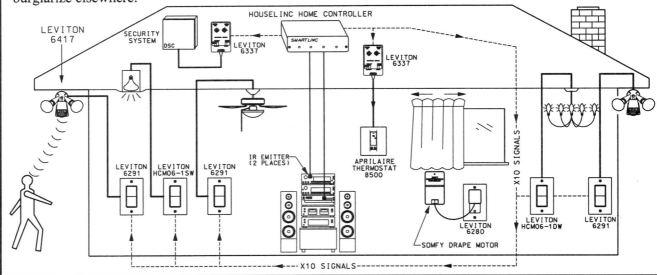

SYSTEM FEATURE 113: JDS INTEGRATED HOME CONTROL SYSTEM

The *JDS Stargate* Integrated Home Automation System is one of the most powerful systems available. *Stargate* can control lighting, appliances, air conditioning systems, ceiling fans, garage doors, property access gates, draperies, sprinkler systems, PBX telephone system, security system and other electrical devices. The home can be controlled at home or from a telephone or PC on the Internet anywhere in the world. This controller has both Digital and Analog Inputs and Relay Outputs and can be easily expanded if more are required. Both LCD and LED keypads are connected to *Stargate* and are used as control interfaces or independent controllers. *Stargate* also offers RS232 and RS485 connections to communicate with other controllers. This system also uses a *JDS* IR-Xpander to provide 2-Way IR control of audio/video equipment. Temperature sensors are also connected to *Stargate* to provide addition inputs.

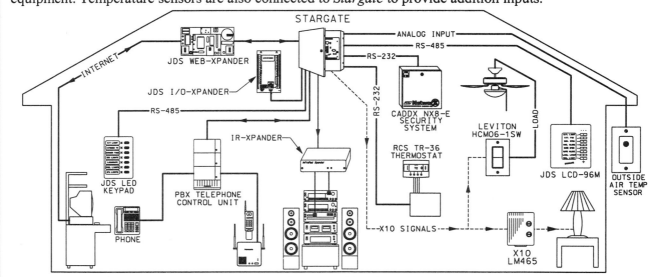

SYSTEM FEATURE 114
SCENE LIGHTING USING THE DHC TOSCANA PROGRAMMER

The Decora Home Controls Scene Capable Receiver switches offer one button programming and provides scene control capability when used with the Scene capable Toscana Deluxe Programmer. Certain model DHC Receiver switches provide 2-Way Communication with the use of the status-tracking-capable Toscana Deluxe Programmer. The Programmer controls up to 256 devices and provides 64 whole house lighting scenes. Created scenes are accessed by using and IR remote or scene lighting control keypads. The Programmer can control electrical loads based on date and time and provides macro-automated programming of lighting and appliances.

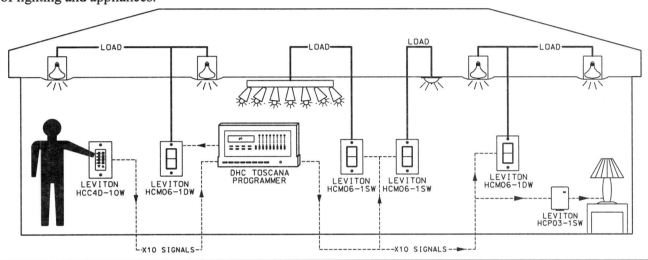

SYSTEM FEATURE 115
AUTOMATIC INDOOR PLANT WATERING SYSTEM

The 'Plantsitter 30' automatic indoor plant watering system waters up to 30 plants. Water flow rates are adjustable and can water plants positioned up to 5 feet above the water storage container. This unit has a built-in timer with manual override. It also incorporates a water level indicator and battery charge indicator. The unit is battery or AC powered. Tubing can be hidden behind furniture. The watering kit includes 50 meters of waterlines, 30 water spikes, 6 waterline connectors, 8 gray drippers and 27 Red drippers.

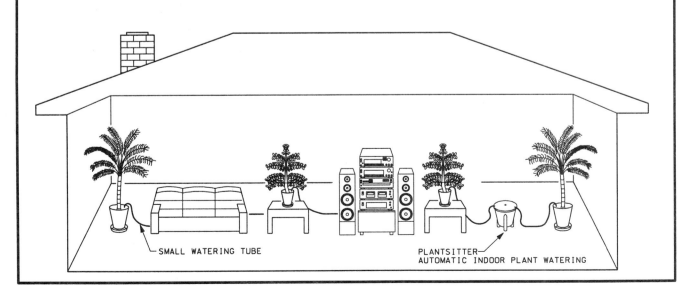

SYSTEM FEATURE 116
AUTOMATED MULTI-ZONE HVAC CONTROL SYSTEM

This multi-zone heating, ventilating and air conditioning system uses the *Stargate* Home Controller in place of a multi-zone HVAC control panel. It also provides advanced automated home control capabilities. The reasons why we can use *Stargate* to replace the multi-zone control panel are the Digital Inputs, Analog Inputs, Relay Outputs and programming capabilities that it provides. In the example shown below, each HVAC Zone has a dedicated in-wall temperature sensor and control damper. If any of the Zones are calling for cooling or heating, *Stargate* will turn ON the HVAC system to provide conditioned air. Air is supplied through a normally open control damper. When a Zone temperature is satisfied, the dedicated Zone damper will be closed.

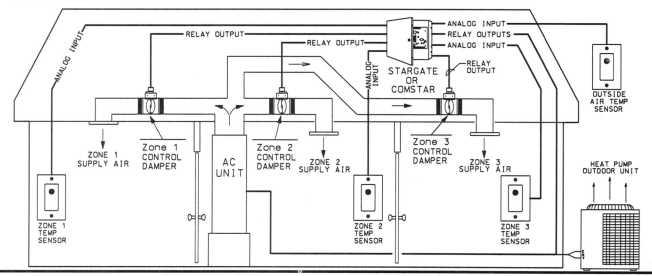

SYSTEM FEATURE 117
ENTERTAINMENT MODE USING ADICON IR AND LEOPARD TOUCHSCREEN

The Leopard Touch Screen/Controller is used to automate the home using If-Then-Else programming Logic that allows the user to build Macros. The Leopard Touch Screen sends and receives X10, IR and ACSII communications. In the example shown below, the touch screen controls lighting and the drapery positioners using X10. Control of the audio/video equipment uses the Adicon IR Output Module. The Leopard Touch Screen/Controller communicates to the Adicon IR module through an RS485 connection. Various modes such as the Entertainment Mode can be initiated from the touch screen, hand-held IR remote or X10 Transmitting device.

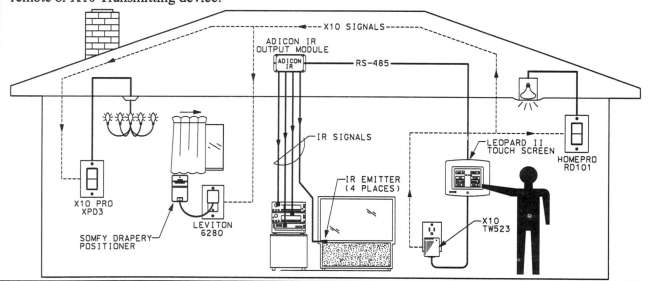

SYSTEM FEATURE 118
RAIN OR HIGH WIND – SPRINKLER TURNS OFF

In the feature shown below, the sprinkler system is interrupted when it rains or when the wind is more than 50 miles per hour. The weather station monitors rain fall and wind speed and when either is above acceptable limits, internal contacts close and provide Digital Inputs to the *CommStar* Home Controller. *CommStar* will then open a Relay Output to stop the sprinkler system pump and open two Relay Outputs to close both sprinkler zone control valves.

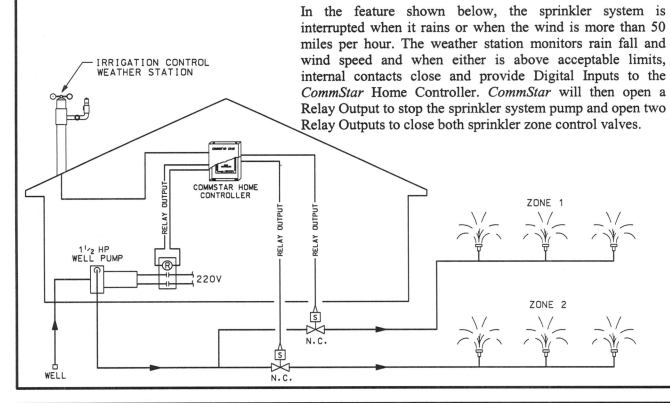

SYSTEM FEATURE 119
HOME MADE X10 SECURITY SYSTEM

When the occupant leaves home she uses keychain remote KR19A to send RF signals that are received by plug-in Transceiver PAT01. The Transceiver then sends X10 signals to both 6280 Receiver receptacles to turn them ON, which arms the system. If a burglar opens a window or door, the N.O. magnetic contacts will close and be sensed by Transmitter PF284. The Transmitter will then send X10 signals to plug-in siren PH508 and low voltage Receiver switch 6337 to alarm the system. On a normal day when arriving home, the occupant will use the keychian remote to disarm the system by turning off the 6280 Receiver receptacles. At bed time the occupant arms the system using tabletop Transmitter MC460.

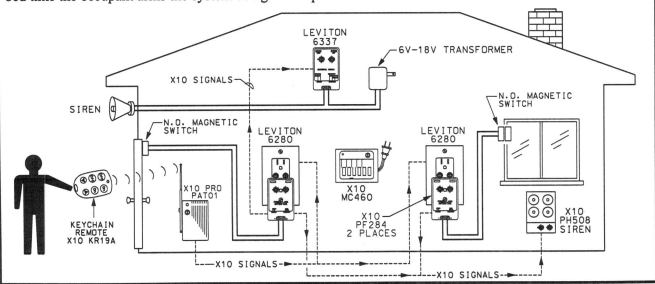

SYSTEM FEATURE 120
TESTING THE HOME PRIOR TO SYSTEM INSTALLATION

The example shown below illustrates a testing procedure to find out whether a home has electrical noise problems or low X10 signal strength areas. Two test components are used. The PowerFlash PF284 Transmitter is used to send continuous ON and OFF X10 signals over the power lines. The other device is an X10 signal Analyzer that reads the signal strength of the X10 signals sent by the PF284 and monitors power lines for electrical noise. The Analyzer also identifies specific X10 codes transmitted, dissects X10 signals on the lower lines and has a test session history recorder. Testing is performed by plugging the Analyzer into the receptacle that will serve the Home Controller. Then plug-in the PF284 Transmitter into each standard power receptacle throughout the home. Monitor the Analyzer for electrical noise and record X10 signal strength readings from each PF284 location. When noise and low signal strength is located, these conditions can be remedied by installing the appropriate components.

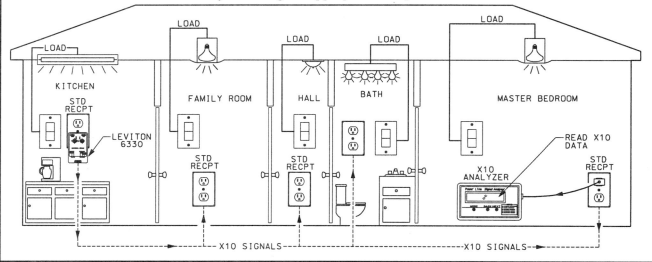

SYSTEM FEATURE 121
METHODS OF ELIMINATING ELECTRICAL NOISE PROBLEMS

X10 signals can be interrupted when excessive electrical noise is present on the power lines, which can cause system control difficulties. After determining the source of noise on the power lines using the system Analyzer, the proper noise filters can be installed. Wired-in noise filter 6287 is installed inside electrical load fixtures such as fluorescent lights. Plug-in noise filter AF100 is used to block noise created by computers and other plug-in electrical devices that draw a maximum of 5A. Plug-in filter AF120 is used to block electrical noise produced by electrical loads that draw up to 15A. Wired-in noise filter 6284 is used to block electrical noise coming from a neighbor's house served by the same power transformer.

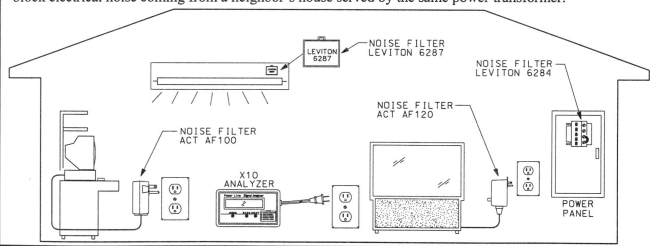

SYSTEM FEATURE 122
SCENE LIGHTING WITHOUT USING A HOME CONTROLLER

This feature allows the user to control multiple rooms, or even all the lights in the home by pushing a single X10 command button on Keypadlinc 12074W without help from a Home Controller. All room lighting can turn ON and OFF to their independent dim level simultaneously and at their own ramp/fade rates. Since the Switchlinc components remember different light settings for a variety of situations, the homeowner can set up different lighting scenes or modes that may include the Romance Mode, Entertainment Mode, Party Mode, etc. Receiver switches that are programmed to respond to each mode will do so by automatically adjusting the lights to a predetermined brightness level. Brightness levels can be between 3% and 100%. With 2-way Receiver switches a user can manually turn ON or OFF the switch and the switch will send out its number code and command code to other Receiver switches in the home for them to respond as well.

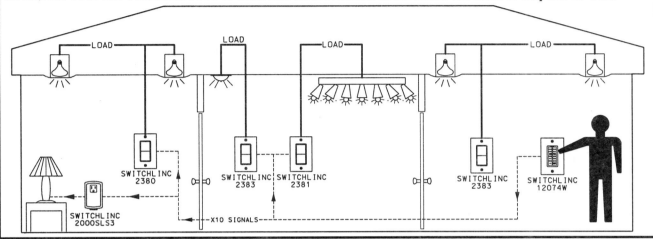

SYSTEM FEATURE 123
HOW TO AUTOMATE LARGE LIGHTING LOADS

This example illustrates a Home Theater with a larger number of lighting fixtures that require a total of 1800 watts. Standard in-wall X10 Receiver switches are not rated to handle this much power, so what can we do? The PCS lighting control module is a good selection for this application because it is rated for 2000 watts total. This Receiver switch is install in a standard 4-gang electrical enclosure and has internal fuse protection. Lighting scenes are controlled by a Home Controller or locally from the 6-button PCS SMST6 Transmitter. The primary lighting scene adjusts the dim level for watching the movie. Another scene will adjust the dim level for people to safely enter and leave the room, and the third scene turns the light ON to 100% bright during periods when the room is being cleaned.

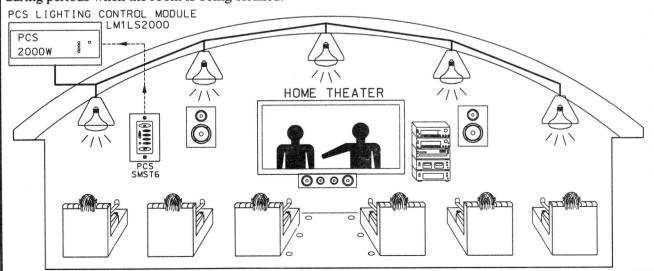

SYSTEM FEATURE 124: PCS SCENE MASTER MOOD LIGHTING

This system feature allows the users to provide different lighting scenes for different occasions similar to Feature 122. This example; however, uses an 8-button PCS SceneMaster Transmitter and two Scene Master Receiver switches to control the lights. The user simply pushes one preprogrammed button on Transmitter SMST8 to provide the Romance mode. Another button may brighten the lights to safely enter and exit the spa, and the third scene may brighten the lights for when the bathroom is being cleaned. The other 4-buttons can be programmed to control other electrical loads in the home.

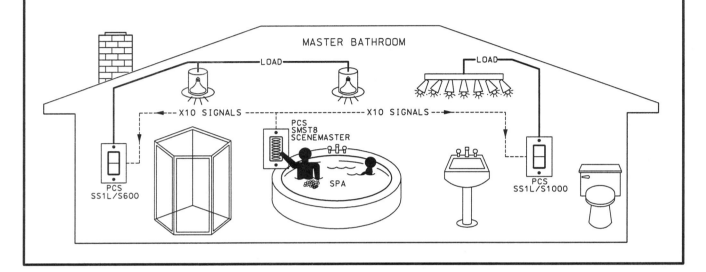

SYSTEM FEATURE 125
REPLACE EXISTING SWITCH WITH A LOAD CONTROL KEYPAD

In this feature we have an existing home where the homeowner wants to incorporate scene lighting. Since he is installing the system himself, he does not want the hassle of having to replace the existing 2-gang switch box with a 3-gang box to provide space to install a Scene Capable Transmitter. In this case there is a separate switch for the vanity lights and the exhaust fan. He can't just take out the light switch and install a wall Transmitter because he still needs a Receiver switch to perform the control functions. He has the option of replacing the light switch with a KeypadLinc. This is because the KeypadLinc is a Receiver switch and Transmitter all in one. The KeypadLinc is wired to the vanity light fixture and is used to control the light and fan using separate buttons. The KeypadLinc is also used to provide multiple lighting scenes in any room in the home when using the SwitchLinc Scene capable Receivers.

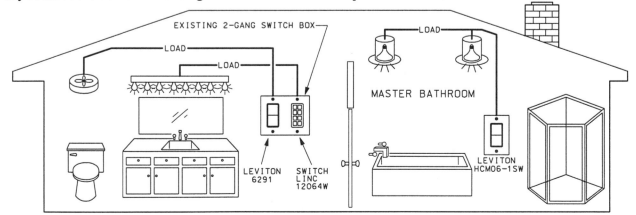

SYSTEM FEATURE 126
HURRICANE SHUTTERS AND DOOR LOCK CONTROL

This feature provides the home with added safety, security and property protection. When the weather station senses a wind speed of 50 miles per hour or greater, a set of internal contacts will close and provide a Digital Input to the Home Controller. The Home Controller will then close Relay Outputs, which in turn closes the motorized hurricane shutters for protection. These shutters can also be controlled closed as part of the Vacation Mode for security purposes. They can be controlled at home remotely using the LCD or LED keypads or X10 Transmitter. Away from the home, the shutters can be control by phone, over the Internet, or from a pocket PC.

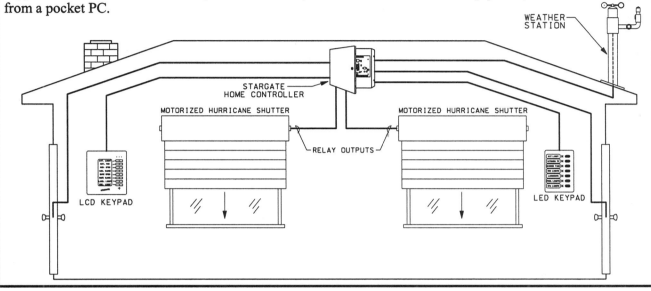

SYSTEM FEATURE 127
WIRELESS DRIVE-UP ANNOUNCER

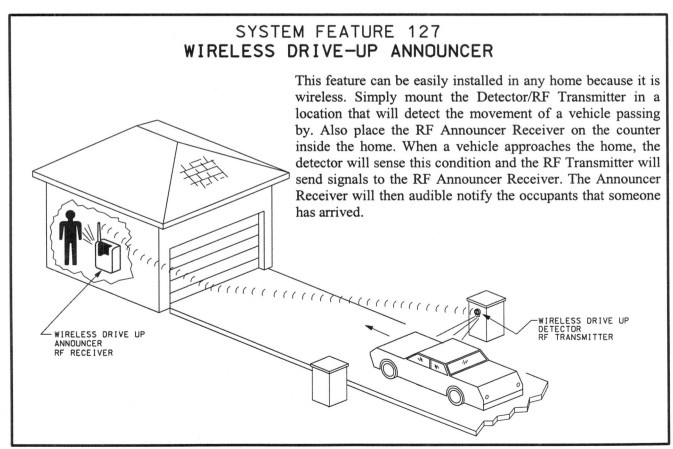

This feature can be easily installed in any home because it is wireless. Simply mount the Detector/RF Transmitter in a location that will detect the movement of a vehicle passing by. Also place the RF Announcer Receiver on the counter inside the home. When a vehicle approaches the home, the detector will sense this condition and the RF Transmitter will send signals to the RF Announcer Receiver. The Announcer Receiver will then audible notify the occupants that someone has arrived.

SYSTEM FEATURE 128
AUTOMATED LANDSCAPE LIGHTING

This feature automatically turns ON the low voltage landscape lighting at dusk and turns them OFF a number of hours later that is user selected. The low voltage lighting transformer is plugged into Receiver receptacle 6280. When Photocell Transmitter 6308 senses approaching darkness, it will transmit X10-ON signals over the power lines to turn ON the 6280 Receiver receptacle that ultimately turns ON the landscape lights. After a pre-selected number of hours, the Photocell Transmitter will transmit X10-OFF signals to turn OFF the receptacle and the lights. The Photocell will also turn OFF the lights when it senses sunrise.

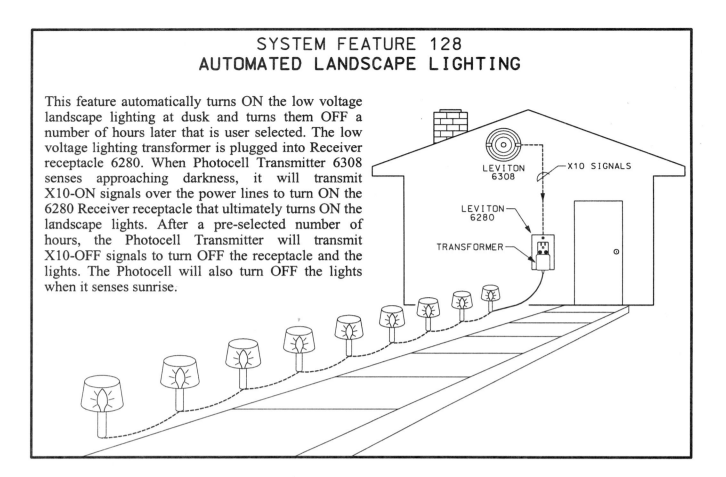

SYSTEM FEATURE 129
AUTOMATED CONTROL WITH MACROS WITHOUT A HOME CONTROLLER

This feature allows the user to easily incorporate up to 42 Macros into the home control system. Macros are programmed to transmit up to 48 X10 commands to control multiple electrical devices in a string one after another. In this application the user pushes buttons A1-ON from the PHC01 tabletop Transmitter. This transmits A1-ON X10 signals over the power lines to be received by the Macro Module. Once received, this triggers a specific Macro that turns one light ON to 50% bright, the other light ON to 20% bright, and turns ON the fan. Imagine having up to 48 electrical devices controlled ON or OFF, dimmed or brightened by one Macro with the push of one button.

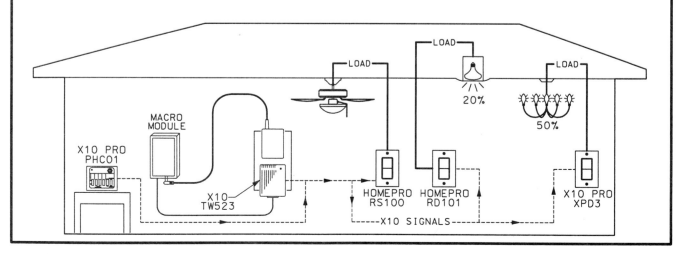

SYSTEM FEATURE 130
ADICON OCELOT LEOPARD HOME AUTOMATION SYSTEM

This home automation system is made up of multiple Adicon modules design to provide specific automated control features. Instead of purchasing an expensive Home Controller that does much more than what is needed by some people, one could purchase the appropriate Adicon modules and add on system capabilities as needed. The Speak Easy module provides pre-recorded messages. The SECU16 module provides Digital or Analog Inputs and Relay Outputs. The SECU16IR module provides IR Outputs, and the RLY8XA module provides 10 amp 240 volt relays. There is also a Home Controller Module OCELOT that is pre-programmed using the PC. The Leopard II Touch Screen can also be used as a controller and provides on screen programming.

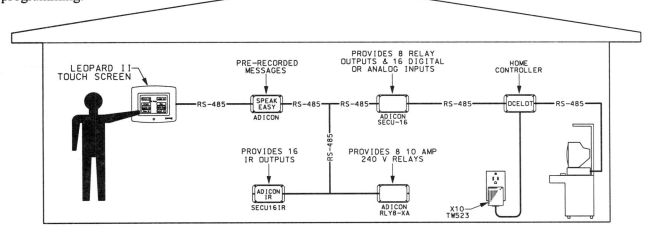

SYSTEM FEATURE 131
ANSWER THE FRONT DOOR OR BACK DOOR FROM THE PHONE

The DoorBell Fon replaces the existing doorbell and allows the occupants to answer the front door or back door from any phone in the home. One keystroke on the phone will also open the door with the optional electric lock controller. When a visitor presses the button on either doorbox, it rings the phones with a distinct ring. If an occupant is on the phone at the time, she will hear a call-waiting signal, which prompts her to push the flash button to answer it. This system can also be used as an indoor intercom.

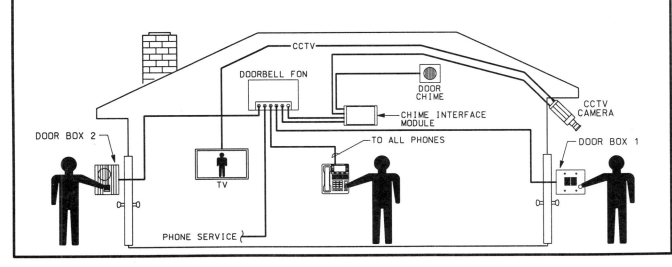

SYSTEM FEATURE 132
AUTOMATED WHOLE HOUSE LIGHTING CONTROL

This feature automatically turns the lights ON when and occupant enters a room and will remain ON while the room is occupied. When an individual enters a room, the motion sensor will detect this person and provide a Digital Input to the Home Controller. The Home Controller will then transmit the appropriate X10 signals to turn the light ON. As long as the Digital Input 'Is ON' the Home Controller will maintain the light ON. If the occupant is no longer present, the Digital Input 'Goes OFF' after a 5 minutes delay. This tells the Home Controller to transmit X10-OFF signals to turn the light OFF. The Home Controller will provide the necessary programming to disable the automatic lighting control functions in the bedrooms after the In Bed Mode as been activated.

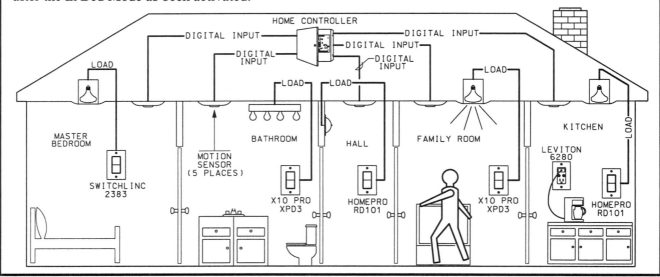

SYSTEM FEATURE 133
HUMIDIFY THE AIR IN DRY CLIMATES

When the air in the home is dry, it can dry out your skin and potentially cause static discharge problems that can affect electronic equipment. When the relative humidity drops below 40% RH sensed by the humidity sensor, the N.O. feedwater solenoid valve opens and supplies water to the humidifier. If the home is calling for heating, the humidifier will sense airflow from the fan and provide a mist directed into the air stream. This operation will raise the RH in the home. When the moisture level reaches 45% RH in the home, the humidity sensor contacts will close and power the circuit to close the solenoid valve. This will stop the flow of feedwater to the humidifier.

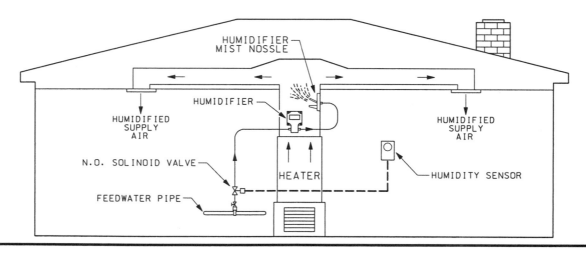

SYSTEM FEATURE 134
SENSING WHETHER A/V EQUIPMENT IS ON OR OFF

One of the main problems with controlling audio/video equipment is that when most home controllers transmit IR signals to activate the Entertainment Mode, for instance, the home controller does not know if any of the A/V equipment is already ON. A/V equipment could have been turned ON by someone using a remote or manually at the unit without the controller knowing it. If a unit is ON, the Home Controller would turn it OFF because IR signals do not have separate ON and OFF command codes. To have the Home Controller read if the A/V equipment is actually ON or OFF, a unit called a 4-Input Box is used in addition to the Home Controller. This device uses up to 4 light sensors. Each sensor attaches to the front of an A/V component and plugs into the back of the 4-Input Box. If the component is ON, the light sensor will detect the light and the Home Controller will not send an IR command.

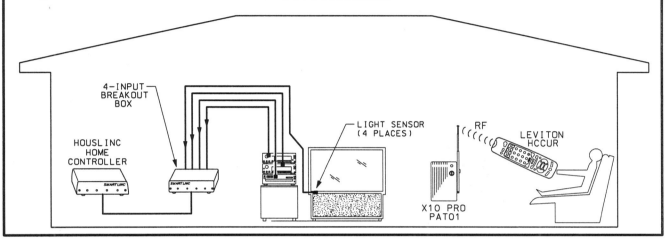

SYSTEM FEATURE 135
WARM UP THE HOME BY PHONE WHILE IN ROUTE

A gentlemen leaves work because he is not feeling well. It is during the winter months and he realizes that his house is probably cold and it would be really nice to arrive home to a warm environment. He calls home and when the Telephone Controller answers the phone, he enters his password to access the system. He then punches in #42, which is the code to initiate the Heating Mode controlled by the RCS TX15 HVAC Controller. After a few seconds he punches in *49, which changes the temperature set-point to 80 degrees F. By the time he gets home it will be nice and warm.

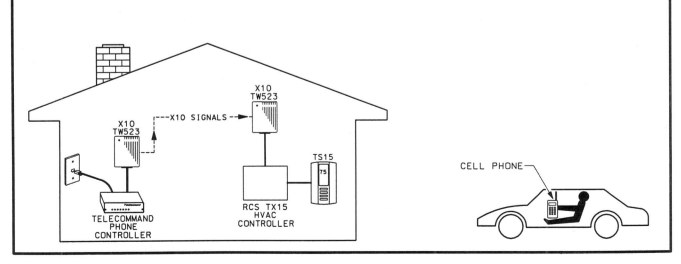

SYSTEM FEATURE 136
SCHOOL BUS ARRIVES IN 10 MINIUTES MODE

The 'Bus-in-10 Minutes' Mode is design to alert a student that the school bus will be arriving at the bus stop in 10 minutes. This mode is very useful for some parents because it is sometimes difficult to get a child to move in the morning. The Home Controller has a built-in clock that is used to flash the child's bedroom and bathroom lights OFF and back ON a few times, so the child knows whether they are running late or on schedule.

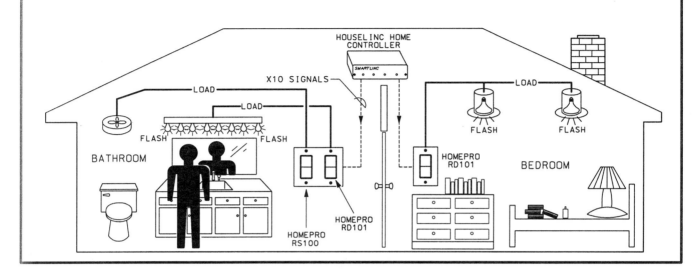

SYSTEM FEATURE 137
3-WAY CONTROL USING REMOTE SWITCH FOR 1000W MAX LOAD

The Dining Room switch on the right side of the room is a HCM10-1SW Receiver switch and the switch on the left side is not a Receiver but is an MS00R-1 remote slave switch that provides 3-way control. This means it does not receive X10 signals; however, the user can manually control the lights from this location. The Dining Room also has two chandeliers that require 350W each. This means that a standard Receiver switch, which is normally rated for 500 to 600W should not be used to control these loads. To power these lights the designer selects a 1000W Receiver switch HCM10-1SW.

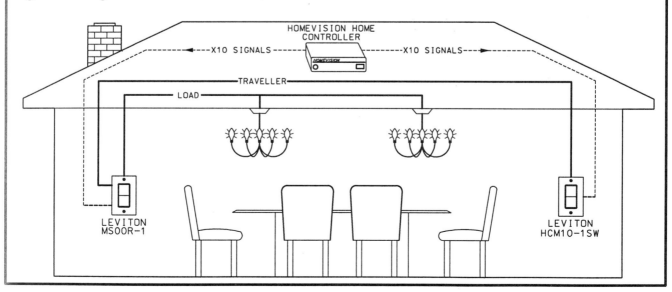

SYSTEM FEATURE 138
THE LEAVING HOME MODE

An occupant is going to leave the home from the front door. On the way out she simply pushes the 'Away' button on the HCC4D wall Transmitter in the Foyer. This sends X10 signals to the Home Controller to initiate the 'Leaving Home Mode'. This mode turns OFF all the lights if it is during the day. If it is after sunset, all the lights except the foyer and the exterior lights turn OFF. This mode also arms the security system, setsback the heating and cooling temperature set-points, turns OFF the water heater, and closes the drapes. The ceiling fans turn OFF and wall receptacles that power potentially dangerous appliances with heating elements are turned OFF. Audio/video equipment turns OFF and the WaterCop leak detection system shutoff valve closes. Basically in this mode the homeowner decides what state she wants each electrical load to be in while she is away from the home. This mode will also initiate periodic change in the state of select electrical loads to make the home look lived in for security purposes.

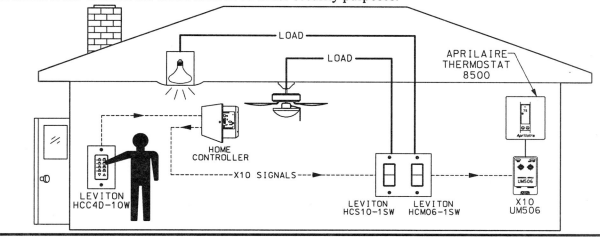

SYSTEM FEATURE 139: RCS INTEGRATED HOME CONTROL SYSTEM

The *CommStar* Integrated Home Automation System is one of the most powerful systems available. *CommStar* can control lighting, appliances, air conditioning system, ceiling fans, garage doors, property access gates, draperies, sprinkler system, audio/video equipment, security system and other electrical devices. Electrical loads can be controlled at home or from a telephone anywhere in the world when using the TeleMaster phone controller. *CommStar* has both Digital and Analog Inputs and Relay Outputs and can be easily expanded if more are required. Both LCD and LED keypads are connected to *CommStar* and are used as control interfaces or independent controllers. *CommStar* also offers RS232 and RS485 connections. This system also uses the IR-Xpander to provide 2-Way IR control of audio/video equipment. Temperature sensors can also be connected to *CommStar* to provide addition inputs.

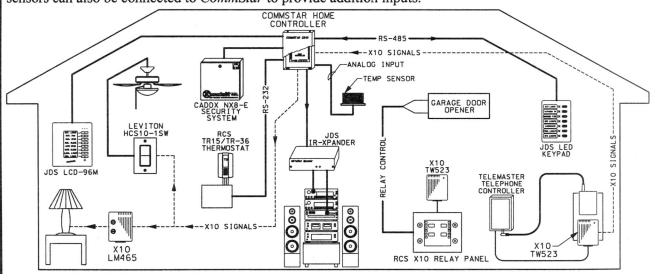

SYSTEM FEATURE 140
ALL LIGHTS ON WITHOUT USING A HOME CONTROLLER

An occupant can control all of the light ON and OFF when the Receiver switches installed throughout the home are set to the same Letter code as Transmitter HCC4A-10W. This particular Transmitter model has the All Lights On/All Units Off buttons and is located at bedside as shown. Only certain model Transmitters have this capability. With these features, the occupant at bedtime only needs to push one button to turn OFF all lights and appliances in the home. This could be considered the Good Night Mode or In Bed Mode without the use of a Home Controller. Although this mode has limited control capability in this particular application, it is still quite convenient. If the occupant hears a noise during the night, all of the lights in the home can be turned ON by pushing of one button for security purposes.

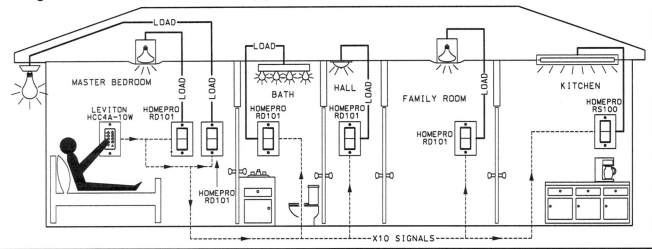

SYSTEM FEATURE 141
ADD A DOOR BELL CHIME TO THE BACK PATIO

In this home it is difficult to here the doorbell ring when the occupant is out on the back patio. An easy method to remedy this problem is to install a PowerFlash PF284 Transmitter wired to the terminals of the doorbell alarm. These are the same terminals that the existing doorbell switch wires are connected to. A chime in then plugged into a 120V receptacle out on the patio. When a friend pushes the doorbell button, the PF284 detects continuity in the circuit and transmits X10 signals to the chime, which alerts the bathing beauty that her friend has arrived.

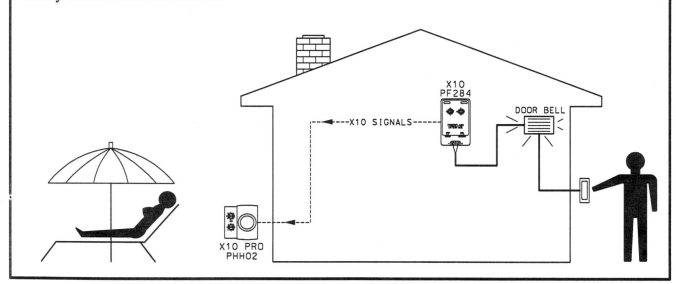

Home Automation System Component Descriptions and Specifications

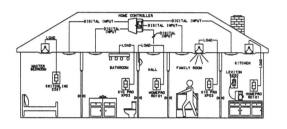

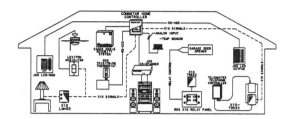

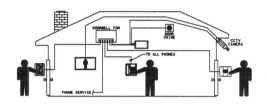

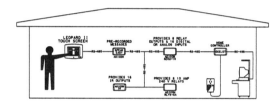

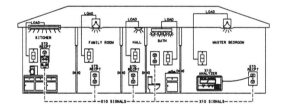

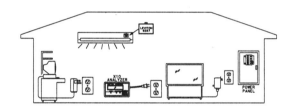

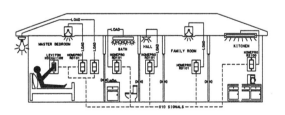

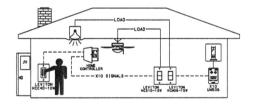

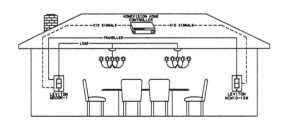

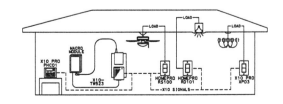

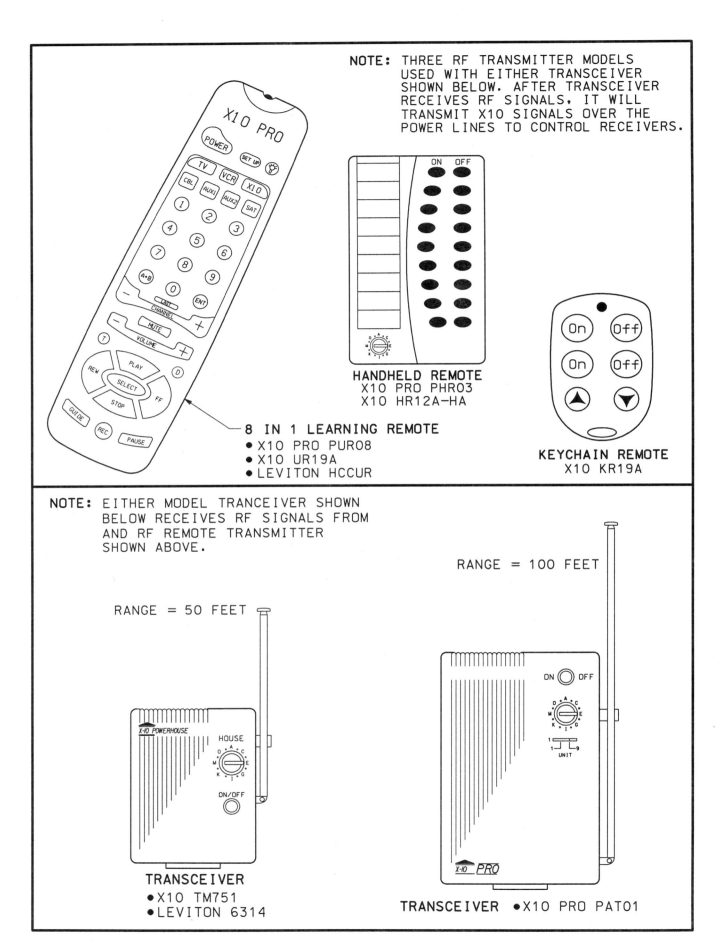

NOTE: THREE RF TRANSMITTER MODELS USED WITH EITHER TRANSCEIVER SHOWN BELOW. AFTER TRANSCEIVER RECEIVES RF SIGNALS, IT WILL TRANSMIT X10 SIGNALS OVER THE POWER LINES TO CONTROL RECEIVERS.

X10 PRO

HANDHELD REMOTE
X10 PRO PHR03
X10 HR12A-HA

KEYCHAIN REMOTE
X10 KR19A

8 IN 1 LEARNING REMOTE
● X10 PRO PUR08
● X10 UR19A
● LEVITON HCCUR

NOTE: EITHER MODEL TRANCEIVER SHOWN BELOW RECEIVES RF SIGNALS FROM AND RF REMOTE TRANSMITTER SHOWN ABOVE.

RANGE = 100 FEET

RANGE = 50 FEET

X-10 POWERHOUSE

HOUSE

ON/OFF

TRANSCEIVER
●X10 TM751
●LEVITON 6314

X-10 PRO

TRANSCEIVER ●X10 PRO PAT01

8-BUTTON TABLE TOP MINI TRANSMITTER   (X-10 MC460)
(X-10 PRO PHC01)

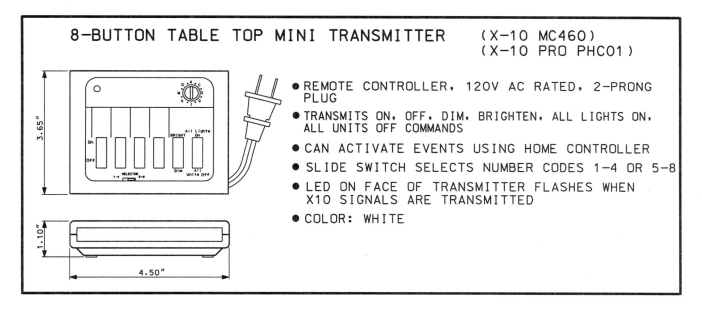

- REMOTE CONTROLLER, 120V AC RATED, 2-PRONG PLUG
- TRANSMITS ON, OFF, DIM, BRIGHTEN, ALL LIGHTS ON, ALL UNITS OFF COMMANDS
- CAN ACTIVATE EVENTS USING HOME CONTROLLER
- SLIDE SWITCH SELECTS NUMBER CODES 1-4 OR 5-8
- LED ON FACE OF TRANSMITTER FLASHES WHEN X10 SIGNALS ARE TRANSMITTED
- COLOR: WHITE

16-BUTTON TABLE TOP TRANSMITTER   (LEVITON 6320)
(X10 SC503)
(X10 PRO PHC02)

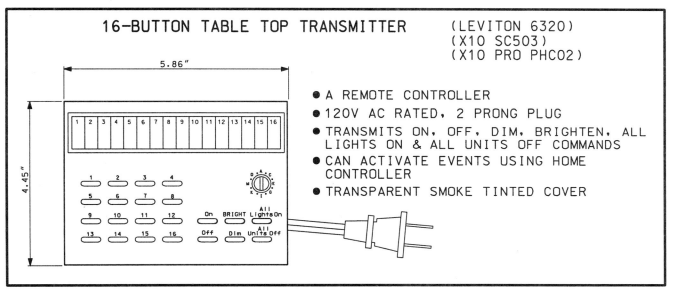

- A REMOTE CONTROLLER
- 120V AC RATED, 2 PRONG PLUG
- TRANSMITS ON, OFF, DIM, BRIGHTEN, ALL LIGHTS ON & ALL UNITS OFF COMMANDS
- CAN ACTIVATE EVENTS USING HOME CONTROLLER
- TRANSPARENT SMOKE TINTED COVER

WIRELESS RF WALL TRANSMITTER (X10 PRO PHW04D)
(X10 SS13A)

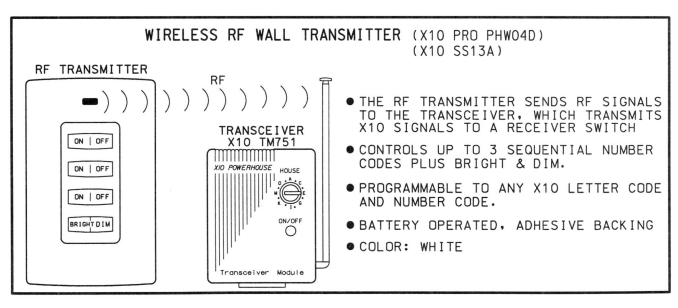

- THE RF TRANSMITTER SENDS RF SIGNALS TO THE TRANSCEIVER, WHICH TRANSMITS X10 SIGNALS TO A RECEIVER SWITCH
- CONTROLS UP TO 3 SEQUENTIAL NUMBER CODES PLUS BRIGHT & DIM.
- PROGRAMMABLE TO ANY X10 LETTER CODE AND NUMBER CODE.
- BATTERY OPERATED, ADHESIVE BACKING
- COLOR: WHITE

IN-WALL MOUNTED CONTROLLER/TRANSMITTER (LEVITON HCC4D-10W)

- PROVIDES ON/OFF SWITCHING, DIMMING AND SCENE LIGHTING CONTROL
- GREEN LIGHT ILLUMINATES TO CONFIRM AN 'ON' COMMAND IS SENT
- INTELLISENSE VIRTUALLY ELIMINATES SIGNAL PROBLEMS DUE TO LINE NOISE
- FOUR SEQUENTIAL ADDRESS DIMMING CONTROLLER

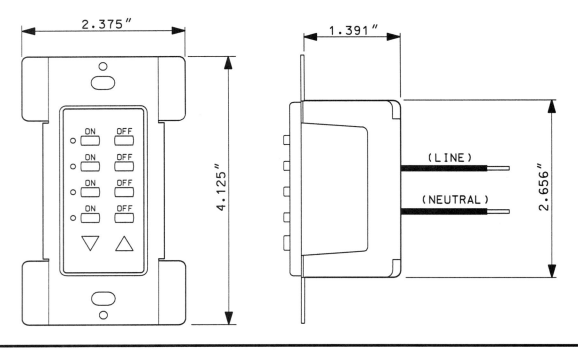

LEVITON WALL MOUNTED 4-BUTTON TRANSMITTER (16400) BASE

- 120V AC RATED, 2 WATTS POWER CONSUMPTION
- ACCEPTS 7 DIFFERENT CONTROLLER FACES
- LED INDICATORS SHOW ON/OFF STATUS OF X10 RECEIVERS
- CONTROL FOUR SEQUENCIAL X10 ADDRESSES
- CAN BE USED TO INITIATE MODES WHEN USING A HOME CONTROLLER

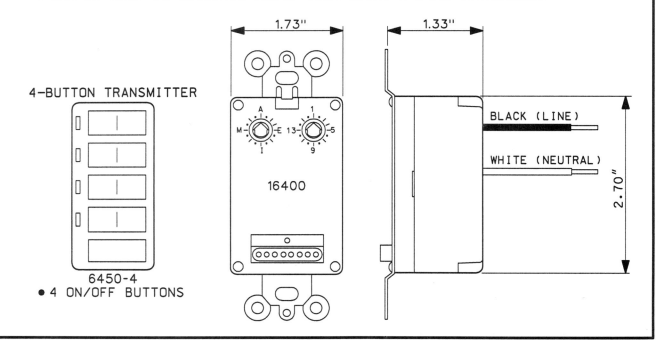

PCS 8-BUTTON SCENEMASTER VERSION 3.0 WALL TRANSMITTER (SMST8)

- BUTTONS ARE PROGRAMMED TO TURN ON AND OFF UP TO 8 SCENEMASTER DEVICES OR OTHER X10 CONTROLLED ELECTRICAL LOADS. SAME BUTTON TOGGLES LOADS ON & OFF. EACH BUTTON WILL LIGHT-UP WHEN LOAD IS ON AND TURN OFF WHEN LOAD IS OFF.

- BUTTONS ARE PROGRAMMED TO CREATE 8 INDIVIDULAL LIGHING SCENES. BUTTON WILL LIGHT UP WHEN SCENE IS ON AND TURNS OFF WHEN SCENE IS OFF.

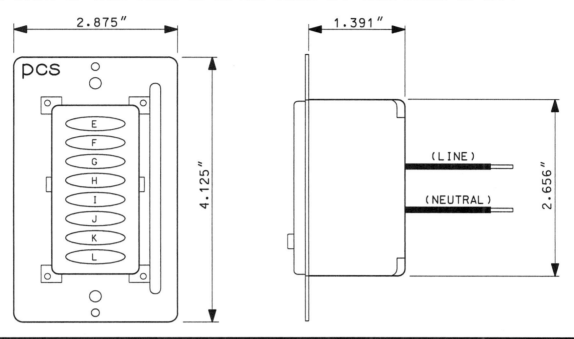

PCS 6-BUTTON SCENEMASTER VERSION 3.0 WALL TRANSMITTER (SMST6)

- PROGRAMMABLE TWO-WAY X10 COMPATABLE TRANSMITTER w/ BACK-LIT BUTTONS
- BRIGHT AND DIM BUTTONS ARE USED TO BIGHTEN OR DIM THE LAST SCENE.
- IR CONTROL, CAN STORE A SERIES OF X10 COMMANDS OR MACROS FOR SCENES
- BUTTONS A, B, C & D CAN BE PROGRAMMED TO PROVIDE FEATURES OF 8-BUTTON SMST8 SCENEMASTER TRANSMITTER SHOWN ABOVE.

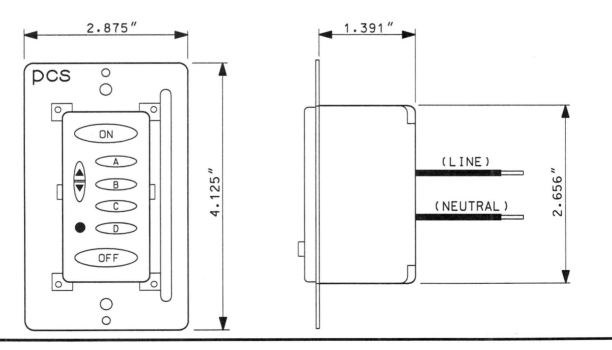

6-BUTTON KEYPADLINC WITH INTEGRATED DIMMER (12063W)

- COMBINES FEATURES OF A SWITCHLINK RECEIVER AND TRANSMITTER IN ONE UNIT.
- REPLACES A SWITCH TO CONTROL THE CONNECTED LOAD AND CONTROLS OTHER RECEIVER SWITCHES.
- CHANGES THE MOOD OF THE HOME'S LIGHTING BY PRESSING ONE BUTTON.
- SEE AT A GLANCE IF LIGHTS IN OTHER ROOMS ARE ON OR OFF.

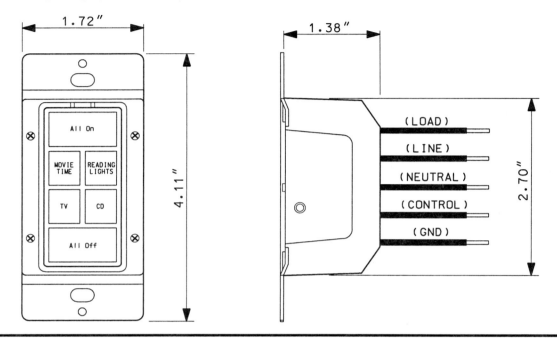

8-BUTTON KEYPADLINC WITH INTEGRATED DIMMER (12064W)

- COMBINES FEATURES OF A SWITCHLINK RECEIVER AND TRANSMITTER IN ONE UNIT.
- REPLACES A SWITCH TO CONTROL THE CONNECTED LOAD AND CONTROLS OTHER RECEIVER SWITCHES AND ELECTRICAL DEVICES AS WELL.
- CHANGES THE MOOD OF THE HOME'S LIGHTING BY PRESSING ONE BUTTON.
- BACK-LIT BUTTONS INDICATE IF LIGHTS IN OTHER ROOMS ARE ON OR OFF.

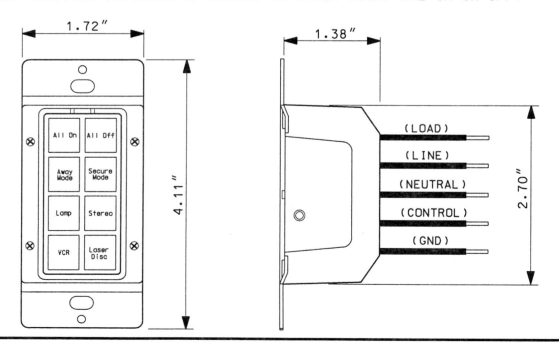

A10 MEMBRANE 8-BUTTON KEYPAD TRANSMITTER (ACT TC184)

- CAN TRANSMIT X10 SIGNALS DIRECTLY TO RECEIVER SWITCHES
- CAN TRANSMIT X10 SIGNALS TO A HOME CONTROLLER TO ACTIVATE MODES
- CONTROLS 4 ADDRESSES, 1 BUTTON ON, 1 BUTTON OFF. CONTROL 3 ADDRESSES PLUS DIM/BRIGHT. CONTROLS 3 ADDRESSES PLUS ALL LIGHTS ON, ALL UNITS OFF CONTROL 8 ADDRESSES, 1 BUTTON ON/OFF PER ADDRESS

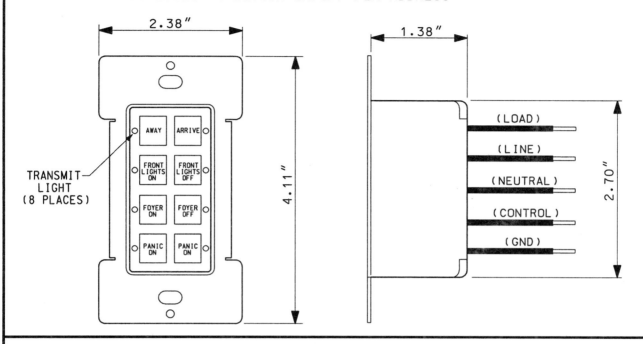

TRANSMITTER POWERFLASH INTERFACE (X10 PF284) (X-10 PRO PSC01) (LEVITON 6330)

- ACTIVATED BY DRY CONTACT or LOW VOLTAGE INPUT (6-18V AC, DC or AUDIO)
- Mode 1 = ALL LIGHTS ON, ALL UNITS OFF
- Mode 2 = FLASH ALL LIGHTS ON/OFF
- Mode 3 = ON/OFF FOR ONE UNIT CODE ONLY
- Input A = LOW VOLTAGE INPUT, Input B = DRY CONTACT CLOSURE
- PLUGS INTO 120V 60Hz RECEPTACLE

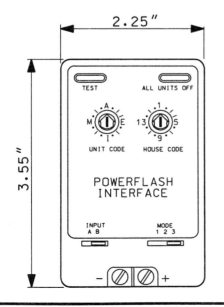

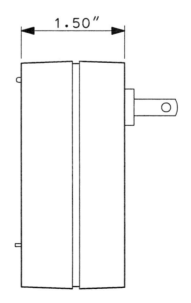

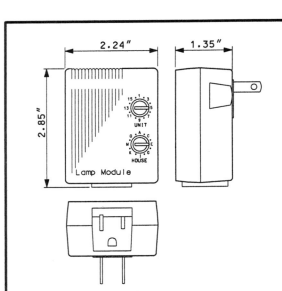

X10 LAMP MODULE (X10 LM465)
(X10 PRO PLMO3)

- CONTROLS INCANDESCENT & HALOGEN LIGHTING
- 300W, 120V AC RATED
- 2 PIN PLUG
- PLUGS INTO 120V RECEPTACLE
- RESPONDS TO ON, OFF, DIM, BRIGHTEN,
- ALL LIGHTS ON, ALL UNITS OFF
- WHITE IN COLOR

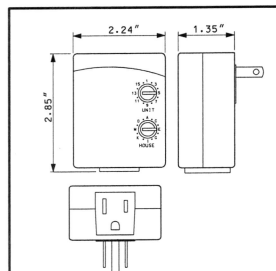

APPLIANCE MODULE (X10 PRO PAMO2)
NO AGC (X10 AM466)

- CONTROLS COFFEE POTS, FANS, HUMIDIFIER, CHRISTMAS LIGHTS.
- 1/3 HP MOTOR LOAD, 15A RESISTIVE
- 500W LAMPS, 120V AC LAMP RATED
- RESPONDS TO ON, OFF, ALL UNITS OFF
- 3 PIN PLUG
- OFFERS AUTOMATIC GAIN CONTROL
- PLUGS INTO 120V 3 PRONG RECEPTACLE
- WHITE IN COLOR
- TWO-WAY APPLIANCE MODULES AVAILABLE

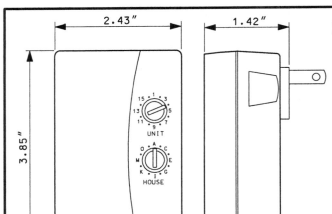

2-WAY LAMP MODULE X10 LM14A

- INCANDESCENT & HALOGEN LAMPS ONLY
- SOFT ON & RESUME DIM — ALSO (AGC)
- RESPONDS TO STATUS REQUESTS
- RESPONDS TO ON, OFF, DIM, BRIGHTEN, ALL LIGHTS ON, ALL UNITS OFF
- PLUGS INTO 120V 60 Hz RECEPTACLE
- 300W, 120V AC RATED

NOTE: A TWO-WAY APPLIANCE MODULE PAM22 IS ALSO AVAILABLE

GREEN LIGHT DIMMER, SCENE CAPABLE RECEIVER (LEVITON HCM06-1DW)

- REMOTE & MANUAL CONTROL - DIMMING LED's, 1 BUTTON PROGRAMMING
- INCANDESCENT & MAGNETIC LOW VOLTAGE CONTROL
- 600W INCANDESCENT, 600VA MAGNETIC LOW VOLTAGE, 125V 60Hz RATED
- RESPONDS TO SOFT ON/FADE-OFF, PRE-SET DIM, ALL LIGHTS ON/ALL UNITS OFF
- TRUE ROCKER-STYLE OPERATION, INTELLISENSE (GATED AUTOMATIC GAIN CONTROL)

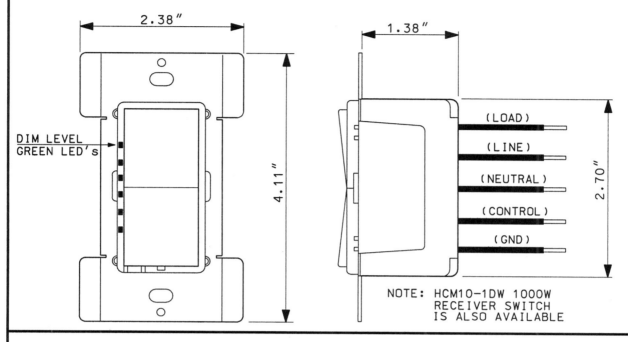

3-WAY REMOTE SLAVE SWITCH (LEVITON MS00R-1)

- INCANDESCENT, MAGNETIC LOW VOLTAGE, FLUORESCENT LIGHTS
- MANUAL ON/OFF AND DIMMING CONTROL
- TRUE ROCKER-STYLE OPERATION
- THIS IS NOT A RECEIVER SWITCH

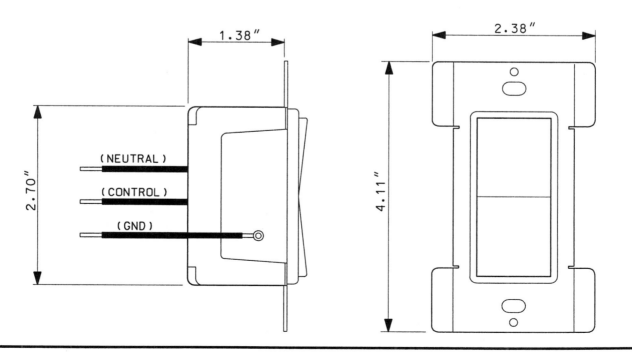

LIGHT DIMMER, SCENE CAPABLE RECEIVER (LEVITON HCM06-1SW)
- REMOTE & MANUAL CONTROL – 1 BUTTON PROGRAMMING
- INCANDESCENT & MAGNETIC LOW VOLTAGE CONTROL
- 600W INCANDESCENT, 600VA MAGNETIC LOW VOLTAGE, 125V 60Hz RATED
- RESPONDS TO SOFT ON/FADE-OFF, PRE-SET DIM, ALL LIGHTS ON/ALL UNITS OFF
- TRUE ROCKER-STYLE OPERATION, INTELLISENSE (GATED AUTOMATIC GAIN CONTROL)

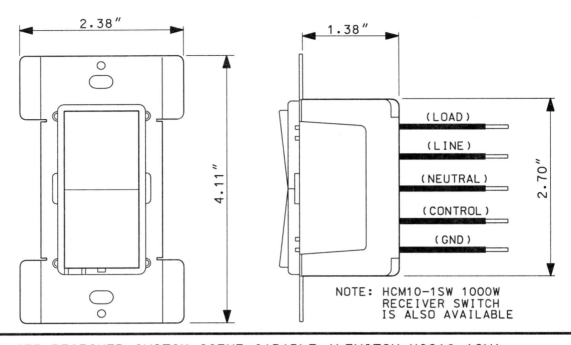

NOTE: HCM10-1SW 1000W
RECEIVER SWITCH
IS ALSO AVAILABLE

ON/OFF RECEIVER SWITCH SCENE CAPABLE (LEVITON HCS10-1SW)
- REMOTE & MANUAL CONTROL – 1 BUTTON PROGRAMMING
- INCANDESCENT, MAGNETIC LOW VOLTAGE, FLUORESCENT, CEILING FAN CONTROL
- 10 AMP 125V 60Hz 1200W RATED
- RESPONDS TO ON/OFF COMMANDS
- TRUE ROCKER-STYLE OPERATION, INTELLISENSE (GATED AUTOMATIC GAIN CONTROL)

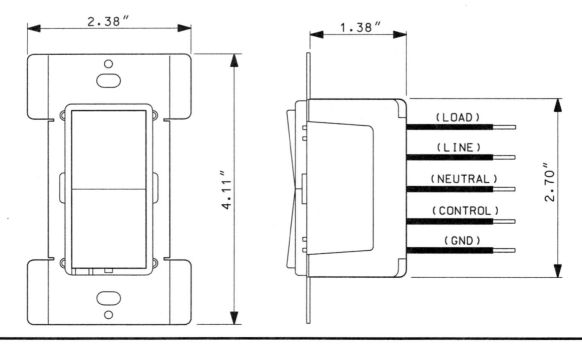

SWITCHLINC DIMMER DIMMER 600 WATTS (2384)

- CONTROL INCANDESCENT, CEILING FANS AND MAGNETIC LOW VOLTAGE LOADS
- SCENE CAPABLE, WHEN TURNED ON IT TRANSMITS COMMAND TO CONTROL OTHER LOADS
- TRUE ROCKER ACTION, TOP = ON/BRIGHT, BOTTOM = OFF/DIM, PRE-SET DIM & RESUME DIM, 8 LEVEL LED SHOWS BRIGHTNESS OF CIRCUIT, STATUS LED SHOW POWERLINE ACTIVITY, ADJUSTABLE FADE RATE AND HAS NIGHT LIGHT INDICATOR
- 3 & 4 WAY READY

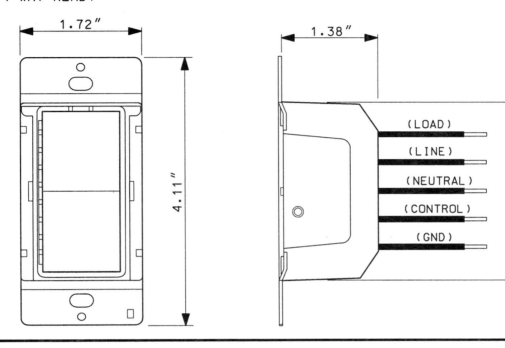

SMARTSWITCH SCENEMASTER VERSION 3.0 (PCS SS1/S-1000) 1000 WATTS

- CONTROLS INCANDESCENT AND MAGNETIC LOW VOLTAGE LOADS
- SCENE CONTROL, TRUE ROCKER ACTION, VARIABLE RAMP RATES
- LED POWER INDICATOR, MULTI-WAY CONTROL, SECURITY FLASH MODE
- POWERLINE SIGNAL MONITOR, INTERNAL SETTING FOR DIMMING

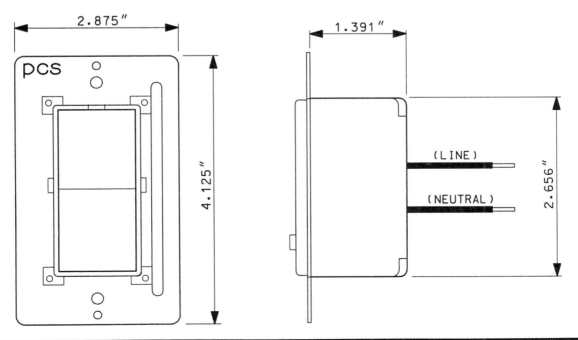

RECEIVER DUPLEX RECEPTACLE (LEVITON 6280) (X10 PRO XPR)

- 15A, 120V AC 60Hz, NEMA 5-15R RATED
- BOTH TOP & BOTTOM OUTLETS ARE SWITCHED
- RESPONDS TO ON, OFF, AND ALL UNITS OFF COMMANDS
- NO MANUAL CONTROL, INTELLISENSE (GATED AUTOMATIC GAIN CONTROL)
- LEVITON RECEPTACLE 6227, TOP OUTLET SWITCHED, BOTTOM REMAINS LIVE

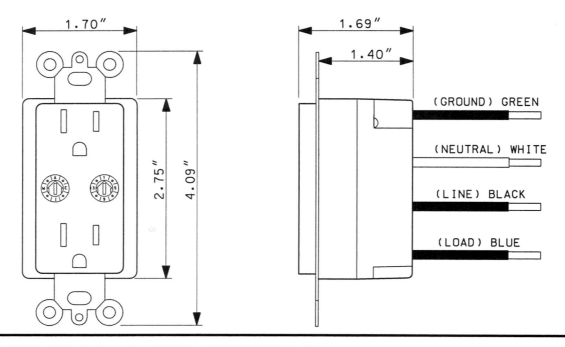

RECEIVER HEAVY DUTY RECEPTACLE (LEVITON 6296)
(X10 PRO XPR2)

- 20A, 120V AC 60Hz, NEMA 5-20R RATED
- RESPONDS TO ON, OFF, AND ALL UNITS OFF COMMANDS
- NO MANUAL CONTROL, INTELLISENSE (GATED AUTOMATIC GAIN CONTROL)
- LEVITON 6298 RECEPTACLE IS RATED FOR 20A, 250V AC 60HZ NEMA 6-20R

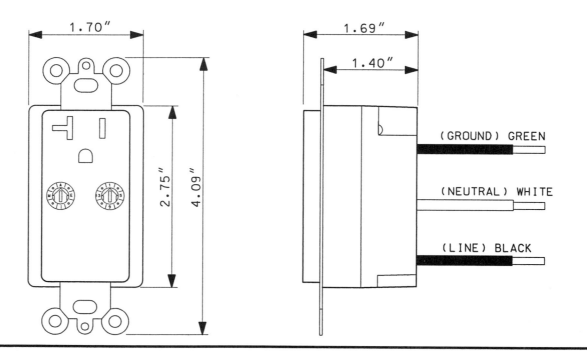

RECEIVER FIXTURE SWITCH MODULE (LEVITON 6375) (HOMEPRO RF104)

- REMOTE CONTROL, NO MANUAL CONTROL
- FOR INCANDESCENT LIGHTING, FLUORESCENT LIGHTS & CEILING FANS
- 15A, 125V AC 60Hz RATED
- RESPONDS TO ON, OFF, ALL LIGHTS ON, ALL UNITS OFF COMMANDS

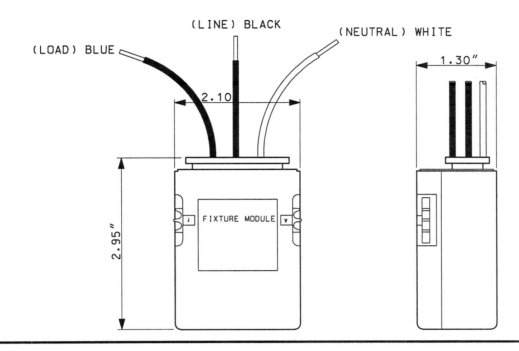

RECEIVER DIMMING FIXTURE MODULE (LEVITON 6376) (HOMEPRO RF114)

- REMOTE CONTROL, NO MANUAL CONTROL
- INCANDESCENT LIGHTING ONLY
- 300W, 125V AC 60Hz RATED
- RESPONDS TO ON, OFF, DIM, BRIGHTEN, ALL LIGHTS ON, ALL UNITS OFF COMMANDS

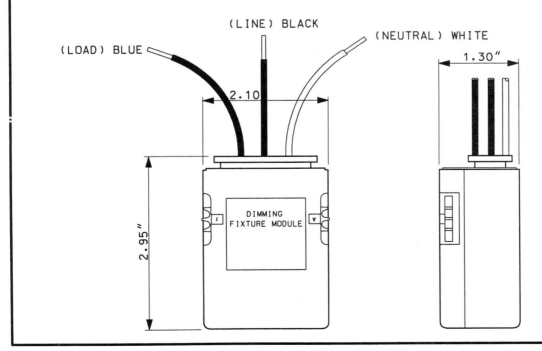

RECEIVER DOUBLE POLE (LEVITON 6371) (X10 PRO XPS2)

- REMOTE CONTROL, NO MANUAL CONTROL
- USE FOR PUMPS, AIR CONDITIONING UNITS, etc.
- 20A, 240V AC 2 HP RATED
- RESPONDS TO ON, OFF, ALL UNITS OFF COMMANDS

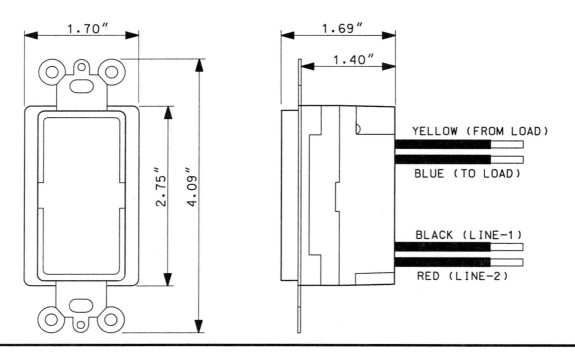

ELK 9100 WATER HEATER AND PUMP CONTROL SWITCH

- USED TO SWITCH 220/240VAC ELECTRICAL APPLIANCES, WATER HEATERS AND PUMPS
- ALSO USE TO CONTROL 110/120VAC BRANCH LIGHTING LOADS
- X10 CONTROLLED, OPTIONAL DRY CONTACT CLOSURE ACTIVATION
- 30 AMP RATED, BUILT-IN SIGNAL BRIDGE, MANUAL ON/OFF PUSH BUTTON CONTROL

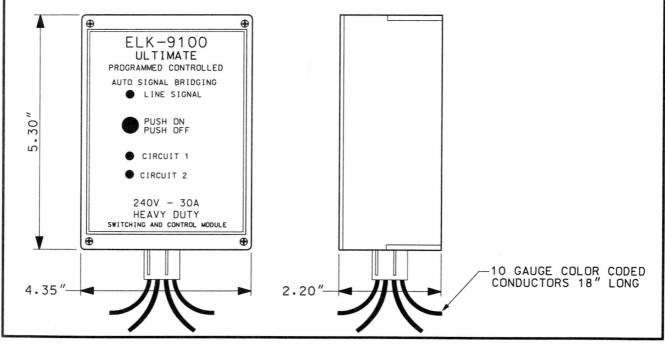

RECEIVER SWITCH UNIVERSAL MODULE

- CONTACTS RATED FOR 5A AT 24V DC & 10A AT 30V AC
- USED TO SWITCH LOW VOLTAGE CIRCUITS
- CONTINUOUS OR MOMENTARY CONTACT CLOSURE
- RESPONDS TO ON, OFF, AND ALL UNITS OFF COMMANDS
- PLUGS INTO 120V 60Hz RECEPTACLE

(LEVITON 6337)
(X-10 UM506)
(X-10 PRO PUM01)

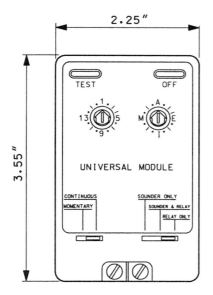
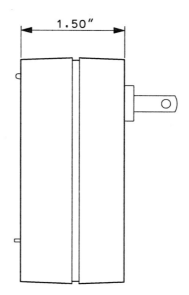

RCS X10 EIGHT RELAY CONTROLLER

- MODEL 8CUXL LATCHING ON OR OFF WITH X10 UNIT ON OR OFF COMMAND
- MODEL 8CUXM MOMENTARY ON WITH X10 UNIT ON COMMAND
- MODEL 8CUXP PULSED ON (1 SEC) WITH X10 UNIT ON AND OFF COMMAND
- RESPONSE TO X10 UNIT CODES SELECTABLE IN TWO GROUPS: 1-8 OR 9-16
- RELAYS: DPDT, 2A 30VDC, .5A 125VAC

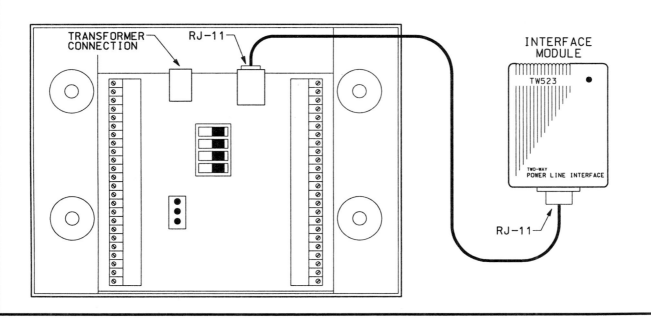

LEVITON X10 COUPLER/REPEATER (LEVITON HCA02-10E)

- TWO PHASE OPERATION
- FOR 120/240V RESIDENTIAL WIRING SYSTEM
- AMPLIFIES X-10 SIGNALS TO OVER 5V AND HAS A BUILT-IN P1 TRANSMITTER
- GENERALLY USED FOR HOMES OVER 2500 SQUARE FEET

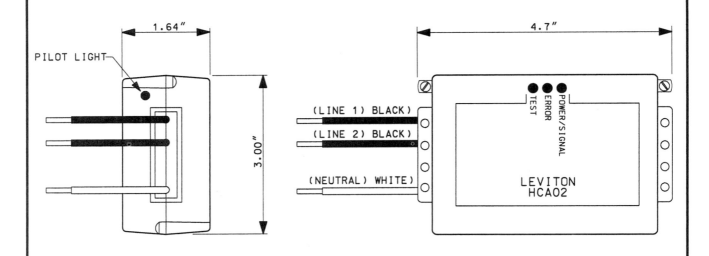

SIGNAL COUPLER/SIGNAL BRIDGE
(LEVITON 6299)
(SIGNALINC 4816H)
(X10 PRO XPCP)

- FOR 120V/240V SPLIT PHASE SYSTEM
- HELPS ASSURE SUFFICIENT SIGNAL STRENGTH THROUGHOUT THE HOUSE

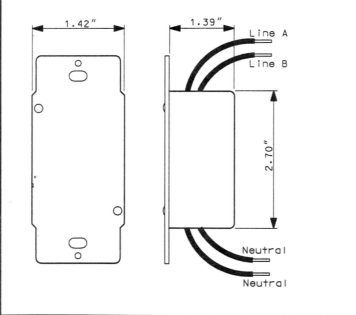

SIGNAL BLOCK COUPLER
(LEVITON 6284) (X10 PRO PZZ01)

- FOR 120V/240V SPLIT PHASE SYSTEM
- BLOCKS X-10 SIGNALS FROM NEIGHBORS WHILE ALSO BEING A SIGNAL COUPLER.
- 200 AMP FILTER

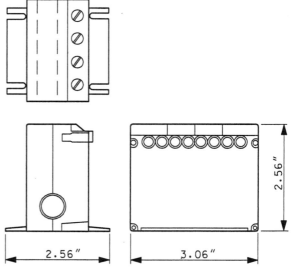

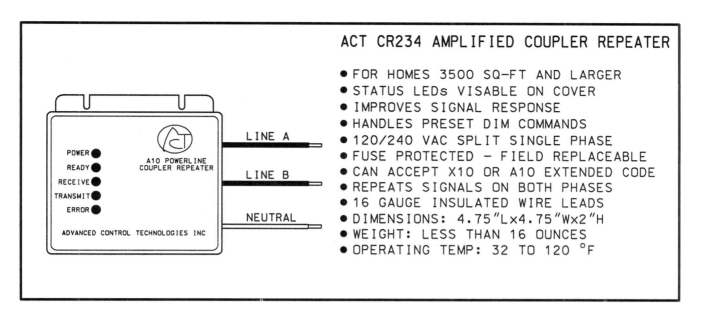

ACT CR234 AMPLIFIED COUPLER REPEATER

- FOR HOMES 3500 SQ-FT AND LARGER
- STATUS LEDs VISABLE ON COVER
- IMPROVES SIGNAL RESPONSE
- HANDLES PRESET DIM COMMANDS
- 120/240 VAC SPLIT SINGLE PHASE
- FUSE PROTECTED - FIELD REPLACEABLE
- CAN ACCEPT X10 OR A10 EXTENDED CODE
- REPEATS SIGNALS ON BOTH PHASES
- 16 GAUGE INSULATED WIRE LEADS
- DIMENSIONS: 4.75"Lx4.75"Wx2"H
- WEIGHT: LESS THAN 16 OUNCES
- OPERATING TEMP: 32 TO 120 °F

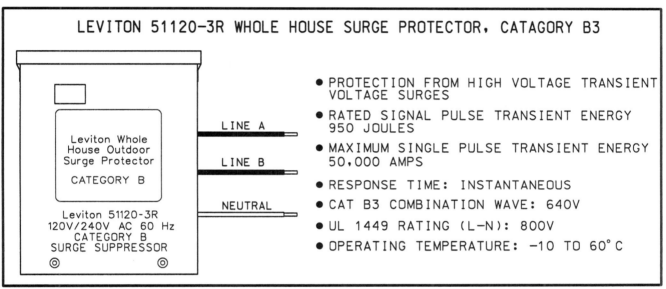

LEVITON 51120-3R WHOLE HOUSE SURGE PROTECTOR, CATAGORY B3

- PROTECTION FROM HIGH VOLTAGE TRANSIENT VOLTAGE SURGES
- RATED SIGNAL PULSE TRANSIENT ENERGY 950 JOULES
- MAXIMUM SINGLE PULSE TRANSIENT ENERGY 50,000 AMPS
- RESPONSE TIME: INSTANTANEOUS
- CAT B3 COMBINATION WAVE: 640V
- UL 1449 RATING (L-N): 800V
- OPERATING TEMPERATURE: -10 TO 60°C

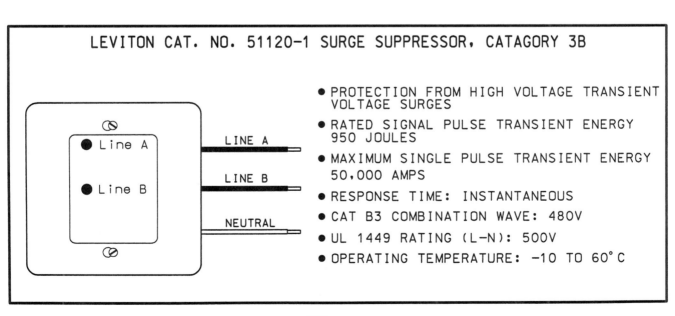

LEVITON CAT. NO. 51120-1 SURGE SUPPRESSOR, CATAGORY 3B

- PROTECTION FROM HIGH VOLTAGE TRANSIENT VOLTAGE SURGES
- RATED SIGNAL PULSE TRANSIENT ENERGY 950 JOULES
- MAXIMUM SINGLE PULSE TRANSIENT ENERGY 50,000 AMPS
- RESPONSE TIME: INSTANTANEOUS
- CAT B3 COMBINATION WAVE: 480V
- UL 1449 RATING (L-N): 500V
- OPERATING TEMPERATURE: -10 TO 60°C

WIRELESS MOTION SENSOR (X10 PRO PMS02) (X10 MS13A)

- SENDS RF SIGNALS TO X10 TRANSCEIVER
- SENDS SIGNALS WHEN ENTERING A ROOM
- PHOTOCELL TURNS LIGHTS ON AT DUSK & OFF AT SUNRISE
- TURNS OFF IN 1 TO 256 MINIUTES (ADJUST)

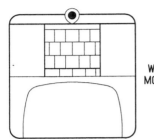

WIRELESS X10 MOTION SENSOR

WIRELESS OUTDOOR MOTION SENSOR (X10 ReX10) (X10 PRO DM10A)

- SENDS RF SIGNALS TO X10 TRANSCEIVER
- SENSOR RANGE: 40', TRANSMIT RANGE: 25'
- PHOTOCELL TURNS LIGHTS ON AT DUSK AND OFF AT SUNRISE
- DOES NOT SEND X10 OFF COMMAND

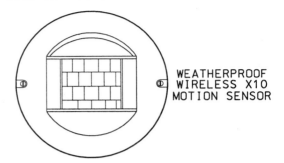

WEATHERPROOF WIRELESS X10 MOTION SENSOR

X10 PH508 POWERHORN REMOTE 110dB SIREN

- TRIGGERED BY X10 ON/OFF SEQUENCE
- TRIGGERED BY POWERFLASH MODULE
- PLUGS INTO A STANDARD POWER RECEPTACLE

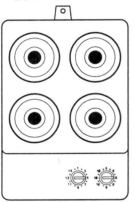
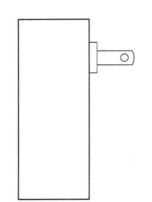

X10 PRO PHH02 X10 CHIME MODULE

- ALERTS OCCUPANT OF AN EVENT
- RECEIVES X10 SIGNALS FROM X10 SECURITY LIGHTS OR TRANSCEIVER/RF MOTION SENSOR COMBINATION
- USE POWERFLASH MODULE TO EXTEND DOORBELL TO ALERT AN OCCUPANT IN BACKYARD

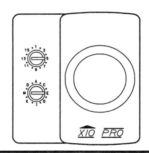
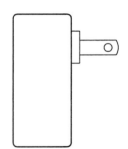

LEVITON 6308 PHOTOCELL TRANSMITTER

- PHOTOCELL SENSES APPROACHING DARKNESS AND RESPONDS BY SENDING X10-ON COMMANDS TO UP TO FOUR X10 DEVICES
- IF DUSK, TURN LIGHTS ON. WHEN 4 HOURS HAS PASSED, LIGHTS ARE TURNED OFF. ALSO TRANSMITS OFF COMMANDS A SELECTED NUMBER OF HOURS LATER

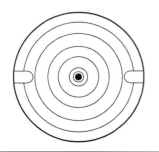
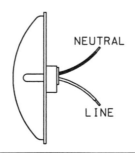

NEUTRAL

LINE

X10 PRO PHC03 SUNDOWNER CONTROLLER

- WORKS SIMILIAR TO 6308 PHOTOCELL
- PLACE NEXT TO WINDOW TO CLOSE DRAPES
- TURNS ON 4 LIGHTS AT DUSK, TURNS 4 LIGHTS OFF AT DAWN
- WORKS SIMILIAR TO 6308 PHOTOCELL

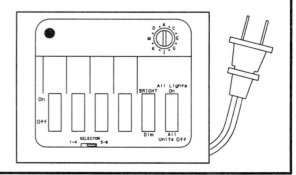

JDS TECHNOLOGIES STARGATE INTERACTIVE INTELLIGENT HOME CONTROLLER

- THIS HOME CONTROLLER FULLY INTEGRATES DIFFERENT SUB-SYSTEMS THAT INCLUDE: LIGHTING, APPLIANCES, SECURITY, HEATING, AND COOLING, POOL & SPA AND IRRIGATION. IR CONTROL OF AUDIO/VIDEO EQUPMENT USING THE IR-XPANDER. USER CAN CONTROL SYSTEM BY TELEPHONE, INTERNET, POCKET PC OR BY VOICE USING HAL2000.

- STARGATE SENDS AND RECEIVES X10 COMMANDS (256 ADRESSES) FOR INTELLIGENT 'IF-THEN-AND-OR-ELSE' CONTROL LOGIC. ALSO SUPPORTS PRESET DIM & STATUS

- OTHER FEATURES INCLUDE: INTERACTIVE VOICE RESPONSE, CALLER ID, VOICE MAIL, LCD & LED RS485 KEYPADS, 2-WAY INFRARED CONTROL AND A WEB INTERFACE.

- OFFERES 16 DIGITAL INPUTS, 8 ANALOG INPUTS AND 8 RELAY OUTPUTS & ASCII.

- ALSO OFFERS 3 RS232 PORTS, 1 RS485 PORT TO INTERFACE PC, MODEM, OTHER CONTROL DEVICES. SERIAL INTERFACE SUPPORTS CADDX NX8-E SECURITY PANEL.

- FOR ALL CONTROLLER FEATURES AND SPECIFICATIONS REFER TO SUPPLIER INFO.

- ALSO INTERFACES LED & LCD KEYPADS, THERMOSTATS, TEMP SENSORS & HUBS.

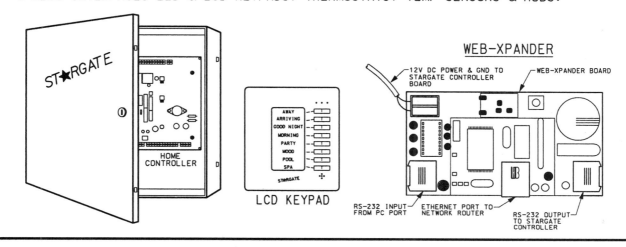

WEB-XPANDER

RESIDENTIAL CONTROL SYSTEMS (RCS) COMMSTAR CS48 HOME CONTROLLER

- SUPPORTS COMMSTAR RS485 NETWORK DEVICES SUCH AS LCD & LED KEYPADS, THERMOSTATS, SENSORS, HUBS, ETC. BUILT-IN SERIAL INTERFACE TO SUPPORT CADDX SECURITY PANEL, 2-WAY X10 CONTROL OF 256 X10 ADDRESSES THAT INCLUDES EXTENDED CODE. OFFERS 'IF-THEN-AND-OR-ELSE' CONTROL LOGIC. MULTIPLE SERIAL PORTS FOR CONNECTIONS TO MODEMS, SECURITY PANEL AND LIGHTING CONTROL. 2-WAY IR CAPABILITY WITH ADD ON JDS IR-EXPANDER. TELEPHONE CONTROL WITH ADD-ON HCTMS TELEMASTER PHONE CONTROLLER.

- FULLY SUPPORTS HOMEVOICE AND HAL2000. TRIGGER WAVE FILES TO BE PLAYED ON PC. ASCII INPUT AND OUTPUT SUPPORT FOR ALL SERIAL PORTS. HVAC SUPPORT OF 32 ZONES USING RCS X10 AND RS232 OR RS485 THERMOSTATS.

- REAL-TIME CLOCK/CALENDAR KEEPS TRACK OF SUNRISE, SUNSET, DAYLIGHT SAVINGS TIME AND LEAP YEAR. REFER TO SUPPLIER FOR ALL FEATURES AND SPECIFICATIONS.

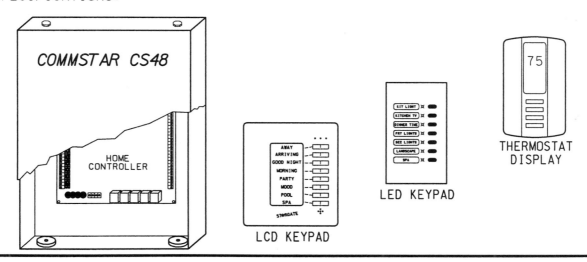

HOUSELINC MODEL 1620B HOME CONTROLLER

- CONTROLS LIGHTING, APPLIANCES, LOCKS, WINDOW COVERING CONTROLLERS, HVAC SYSTEMS, SECURITY, SPRINKLER SYSTEM, AND OTHERS.
- CONTROL ANY OF THE 256 X10 ADDRESSES.
- CONTROLS AUDIO/VIDEO EQUIPMENT THROUGH 4 PROGRAMMABLE IR OUTPUT ZONES.
- DETECTOR PROBES ALLOW HOUSELINC TO SENSE IF AUDIO/VIDEO DEVICES ARE ON OR OFF WHEN CONNECTING OPTIONAL BREAKOUT BOX.
- OFFERS LARGE INFRARED CONTROL LIBRARY ON BOARD.

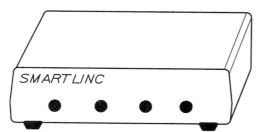 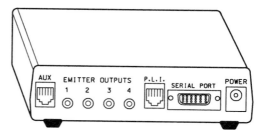

HOMEVISION HOME CONTROLLER

- CONTROL THE ENTIRE HOME WITH A HAND-HELD REMOTE WHILE WATCHING TV. VIEW A COMPLETE SYSTEM INTERFACE ON THE TV SCREEN.
- HAVE THE NAME AND PHONE NUMBER OF CALLERS APPEAR ON YOUR TV.
- VIDEO OUTPUT DISPLAYS MENUS AND CONTROL SCREENS ON THE TV. TWO-WAY IR AND TWO-WAY X10 CAPABILITY.
- 24 DIGITAL INPUTS/OUTPUTS., BATTERY BACK-UP CONTROLS EVENTS BASED ON TIME, DATE, SUNSET, SUNRISE, ETC.
- WEB SERVER PROVIDES CONTROL FROM ANY WEB BROWSER ANYWHERE IN THE WORLD.

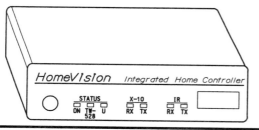 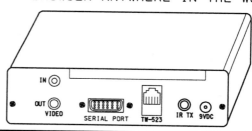

DHC TOSCANA DELUXE PROGRAMMER

- PROGRAMMER FEATURES 2-WAY COMMUNICATION AND IS A SIMPLE CENTRAL ACCESS CONTROL STATION THAT EXPANDS DHC CONTROL CAPABILITY. THIS DEVICE GIVES THE HOME A VARIETY OF MODES AND LIGHTING SCENES WHEN USING DHC SCENE CAPABLE DHC RECEIVER SWITCHES.
- PERMITS CONTROL OF UP TO 256 DEVICES AS WELL AS COMPLEX DATE/TIME AND MACRO AUTOMTED PROGRAMMING OF ELECTRICAL LOADS VIA X10 SIGNALS FROM AN RS-232 PC, HVAC AND SECURITY SYSTEM ENABLED DEVICES. CAPABLE OF PROVIDING 64 LIGHTING SCENES.

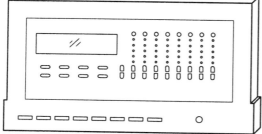

- TIMED EVENT CAN BE SELECTED AND RUN ON A RECURRING BASIS USING A HIGHLY ACCURATE INTERNAL ASTRONOMICAL CLOCK.

- THIS DEVICE REGISTERS STATUS CHANGES WHEN RECEIVERS WITH 2-WAY COMMUNICATION ARE MANUALLY CHANGED.

- FITS IN STANDARD 4-GANG WALL BOX. COLOR IS WHITE.

MACRO MODULE 42IR FOR X10 AND IR SIGNALS

- THE MACRO MODULE ALLOWS THE USER TO PERFORM A MACRO (SEQUENCE OF X10 COMMANDS) BASED ON A SINGLE X10 TRANSMISSION RECEIVED BY THE MACRO MODULE. EXAMPLE: WHEN THE MACRO MODULE RECEIVES AN X10 CODE (A1), THIS TRIGGERS A MACRO THAT DIMS THE LIGHTS, CLOSES THE DRAPES, TURNS ON THE TV AND OTHER AUDIO/VIDEO EQUIPMENT AND TURNS OFF PERIMETER LIGHTING.

- EACH MACRO CAN CONTAIN UP TO 48 X10 COMMANDS. PROGRAM UP TO 42 MACROS.

- MACRO MODULE 42IR FEATURES IR CONTROL OF AUDIO/VIDEO EQUIPMENT AND TIMERS. LEARNS UP TO 27 CODES FROM A HANDHELD REMOTE TO INITIATE A MACRO. HOLDS UP TO 32 TIMERS TO INITIATE ANOTHER MACRO FROM 2 MINIUTES TO 8$\frac{1}{2}$ HOURS AFTER A MACRO HAS BEEN TRANSMITTED. REQUIRES AN X10 TW523 INTERFACE.

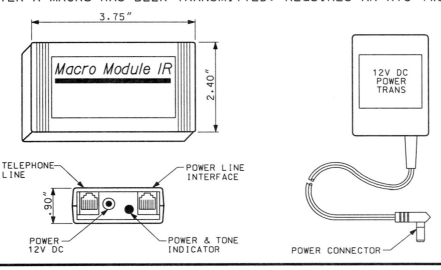

JDS TECHNOLOGIES INFRARED XPANDER CONTROLLER

- THE IR-XPANDER IS A MULTI-FUNCTIONAL TWO-WAY CONTROLLER THAT ALLOWS CENTRALIZED CONTROL OF AUDIO/VIDEO EQUIPMENT THROUGHOUT THE HOME.

- IN THE XPANDER MODE, THE IR-XPANDER CONNECTS TO THE AUX PORT OF A COMPATABLE HOME CONTROLLER.

- IN THE SERIAL MODE THE IR-XPANDER CONNECTS TO THE SERIAL PORT. IT CAN BE OPERATED FROM ANY COMPUTER CAPABLE OF SENDING/RECEIVING ASCII COMMANDS VIA RS-232. THE IR-XPANDER CAN ALSO RESPOND TO IR COMMANDS RECEIVED FROM ANY IR REMOTE.

- THE IR-XPANDER HAS FOUR SEPERATE ZONE EMITTER OUTPUTS TO DISTRIBUTE IR COMMANDS TO MULTIPLE ROOMS. THIS ALLOWS INDIVIDUAL CONTROL OF MULTIPLE TVs, VCRs, ETC. INCLUDING AUDIO/VIDEO COMPONENTS THAT RESPOND TO THE SAME IR COMMAND CODES.

- OPTIONAL POWER STATUS SENSORS CAN BE CONNECTED TO REPORT ON/OFF STATUS OF UP TO 4 COMPONENTS, REGARDLESS OF HOW THE EQUIPMENT WAS TURNED ON.

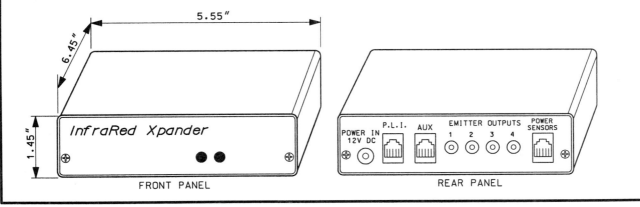

FRONT PANEL   REAR PANEL

ADICON OCELOT 2-WAY INTELLEGENT CONTROLLER WITH BUILT-IN IR CONTROL

- AUTOMATE WITH FULLY PROGRAMMABLE 'IF-THEN--ELSE' CONTROL
- TWO-WAY X10 COMMUNICATION. INFRARED SENDS AND RECEIVES. HAS REAL TIME CLOCK, RS-485 EXPANSION TO ADICON I/O.
- AUTOMATE LIGHTING, APPLIANCES, HVAC SYSTEM, POOLS & SPAS, SPRINKLER SYSTEM, AUDIO/VIDEO EQUIPMENT, DRAPERY CONTROL, FIRE AND SECURITY MONITIORING AND CCTV SYSTEM.
- USE WITH COMPUTER FRONT-END OR AS A STAND ALONE CONTROLLER
- EXPANDABLE SYSTEM. REFER TO SUPPLIER FOR FURTHER INFORMATION.

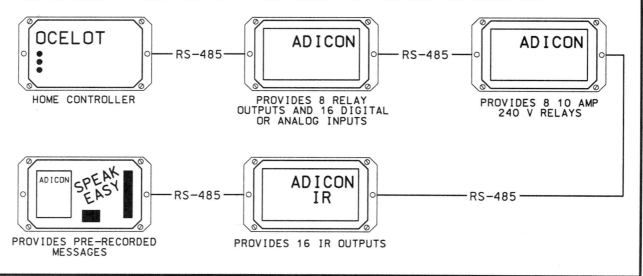

HAL2000 VOICE CONTROLLER PROVIDES HOME AUTOMATED LIVING

- CONTROL ALL ELECTRICAL LOADS WITH SIMPLE VOICE COMMANDS. SPEAK INTO ANY OPEN MICROPHONE CONNECTED TO COMPUTER OR SPEAK INTO THE PHONE AT HOME OR ANY WHERE IN THE WORLD. SAY "CHANGE TEMPERATURE TO 70 F" OR "ARM SECURITY SYSTEM".
- ASK THE COMPUTER TO OPEN THE TV LISTING AND HAVE HAL TELL YOU WHAT IS ON TV AT 10:00 PM.
- HAL CAN ANNOUNCE WHO IS CALLING BEFORE YOU PICK-UP THE PHONE.
- HAVE HAL GET YOU INFORMATION FROM THE INTERNET WITHOUT WASTING TIME SURFING. GOES TO THE INTERNET AS OFEN AS YOU WANT TO RETRIEVE INFO ON: WEATHER, NEWS, E-MAIL, SPORTS, STOCK AND MORE.
- HAL USES CONTINUOUS SPEECH RECOGNITION TECHNOLOGY SURFING. GOES TO THE INTERNET AS OFTEN AS YOU WANT TO RETRIEVE DATA.

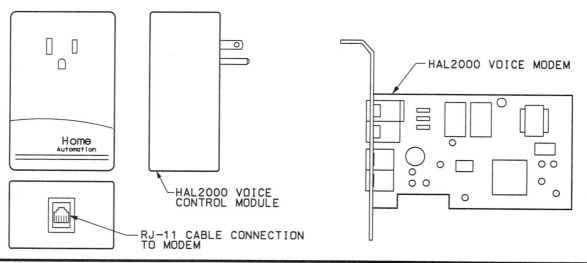

LEOPARD II TWO-WAY INTELLIGENT TOUCH SCREEN CONTROLLER

- THE HOME CONTROLLER IS BUILT INTO THE TOUCH SCREEN.
- ON SCREEN PROGRAMMING. SEND AND RECEIVE X10, IR ANS ASCII COMMUNICATIONS. PROVIDES 2000 PROGRAMMING LINES OF SIMPLE 'IF-THEN AND-OR-ELSE LOGIC TO BUILD POWERFUL MACROS.
- IR LEARNING CAPABILITY.
- HIGHLY EXPANDABLE SYSTEM THAT CAN HAVE 128 ADICON MODULES CONNECTED TO IT IN ANY COMBINATION. PROVIDE DISCRETE OUTPUTS, HIGH CURRENT RELAY CLOSURES, VOICE PLAYBACK MESSAGES AND ROUTER IR CAPABILITIES.
- CONNECTIONS ON REAR PANEL. MOUNTS FLUSH TO WALL.

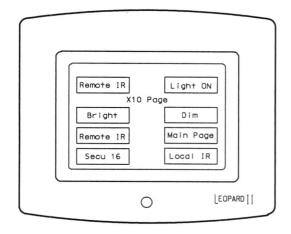

X10 TW523 INTERFACE MODULE

- TWO-WAY POWER LINE INTERFACE
- O.E.M. PRODUCT TO TRANSMIT AND RECEIVE DIGITAL DATA COMPATIBLE w/X-10
- PLUGS INTO 120V 60Hz RECEPTACLE

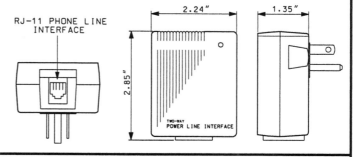

LCD & LED SYSTEM CONTROL KEYPADS

- THIS LCD MULTI-MENU KEYPAD PROVIDES MENU DRIVEN CONTRIOL OF THE ENTIRE STARGATE OR COMMSTAR SYSTEM. FROM ANY KEYPAD THE USER CAN SELECT ANY MODE (AWAY, GOOD NIGHT, VACATION), CONTROL LIGHTS, ADJUST THERMOSTATS, ARM/DISARM THE SECURITY SYSTEM, A/V EQUIPMENT, POOL/SPA, REVIEW VOICE MAIL, DISPLAY CALLER ID, SEND MESSAGES, SCHEDULE REMINDERS, MONITORS SYSTEM ACTIVITY AND MORE.
- EACH KEYPAD STORES UP TO 96 USER-DEFINED MENUS, WHICH CAN BE INDIVIDUALLY CUSTOMIZED WITH TEXT AND GRAPHICS FOR EASY OPERATION, PLUS PREDEFINED MENUS FOR CALLER ID, THERMOSTATS AND VOICE MAIL.
- THE LCD KEYPAD ALSO HAS 3 LEDs USED AS SIGNALS OR STATUS INDICATORS. AREAS REQUIRING ONLY SEVERAL CONTROL FUNCTIONS CAN USE THE LED KEYPAD.

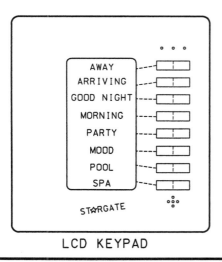

LCD KEYPAD

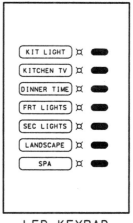

LED KEYPAD

TELECOMMAND PHONE CONTROLLER

- TURNS EVERY PHONE IN THE HOME OR ANYWHERE IN THE WORLD INTO A POWERFUL HOME CONTROL INTERFACE. WORKS WITH ANY TOUCH-TONE PHONE INCLUDING CORDLESS PHONES, CELL PHONES, AUTO DIALER OR VOICE DIALER.

- SIMPLE TOUCH-TONE COMMANDS CONTROL ANY AUTOMATED ELECTRICAL DEVICE. BY SIMPLY PRESSING * FOR AN ON COMMAND OR # FOR AN OFF COMMAND FOLLOWED BY THE X10 RECEIVER ADDRESS CONTROLS THE LOAD REMOTELY. IT CAN ALSO BE USED TO TRIGGER ANY MODE.

- THE TELECOMMAND OFFERS 90 ON/OFF, DIM AND BRIGHTENING COMMAND CODES FOR HOUSE CODES A-J AND UNIT CODES 1-9. THERE ARE ALSO 10 ALL LIGHTS ON, ALL UNITS OFF COMMAND CODES FOR HOUSE CODES A-J.

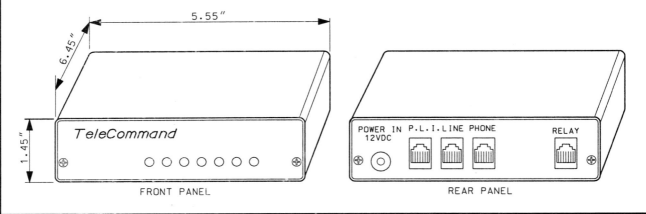

FRONT PANEL   REAR PANEL

TELEMASTER PHONE CONTROLLER

- THE TELEMASTER CONVERTS ANY TOUCH TONE PHONE INTO AN X10 TRANSMITTER. AND/OR INTERCOM SYSTEM. THIS DEVICE CAN TRANSMIT UP TO 256 X10 CODES. EITHER 9, 90, 160 OR 256 CODES ARE AVAILABLE DEPENDING ON DIP SWITCH 1 & 2 POSITION.

- WHEN A LAMP RECEIVER SWITCH IS ADDRESSED AS A1, PUSHING *11 WILL TURN THE LAMP ON AND #11 WILL TURN THE LAMP OFF. TO DIM THE LIGHT, A *11 COMMAND MUST FIRST BE SENT WHILE HOLDING DOWN THE LAST BUTTON PRESSED. TO BRIGHTEN LIGHT, THE USER WOULD RELEASE THE BUTTON AND THEN HOLD IT BACK DOWN UNTIL THE DESIRE BRIGNTNESS LEVEL IS REACHED.

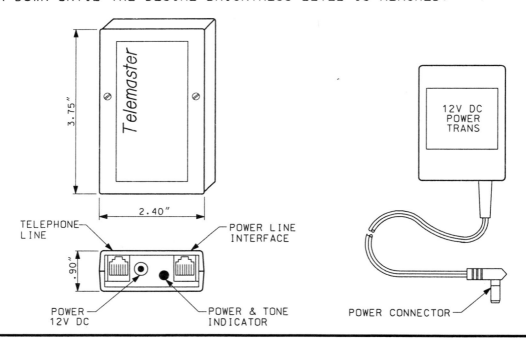

OMNI PRO II INTEGRATED HOME AUTOMATION AND SECURITY SYSTEM CONTROLLER

- THIS SYSTEM ACCEPTS STANDARD SENSORS FOR INTRUSION, FIRE AND TEMPERATURE. CONTROLS LIGHTS, HEATING AND COOLING SYSTEM, APPLIANCES FOR COMFORT, CONVENIENCE, PEACE OF MIND AND ENERGY SAVINGS. OMNI OPERATES BY MODES. DAY MODE, NIGHT MODE, MORNING MODE, AWAY MODE, VACATION MODE AND SO ON. MODES ARE INITIATED BY OMNI AFTER RECEIVING X10 SIGNALS, DATE AND TIME OF DAY AND SUNRISE AND SUNSET TIMES. MODES CAN BE SET UP BY USING THE CONSOLE OR A PC. SECURITY SENSORS MAY BE USED TO ADJUST LIGHTS, APPLIANCES AND TEMPERATURE EVEN WHEN THE SECURITY SYSTEM IS DISARMED.

- FEATURES I/O INPUT/OUTPUT CONTROL. CONTROL SECURITY SYSTEM, LIGHTING, HVAC, ETC, VIA PHONE AT HOME OR ANY WHERE IN THE WORLD. AUDIO/VIDEO CONTROL USING HAI PROLINK. CONTROL LIGHTING VIA X10, RS232/RS485 FOR SERIAL CONTROLLED SYSTEMS. RELAY OUTPUTS TO CONTROL CONTACTORS.

- CONTROL THE HOME AND SEE OMNI SYSTEM STATUS OVER THE INTERNET ANY WHERE IN THE WORLD USING WEB-LINK.

- SUPPORTS 96 SECURITY ZONES, HARDWIRED/WIRELESS, 16 KEYPADS, MULTIPLE PARTITIONS AND CENTRAL STATION REPORTING.

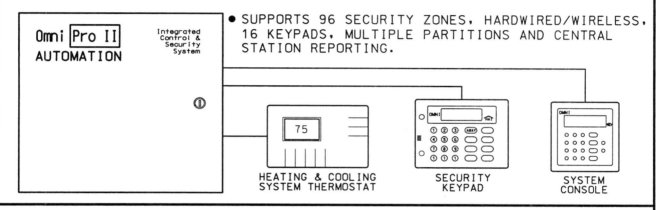

HEATING & COOLING SYSTEM THERMOSTAT   SECURITY KEYPAD   SYSTEM CONSOLE

CADDX NETWORX NX8-E SECURITY SYSTEM

- CADDX INTERFACES STARGATE OR COMMSTAR THROUGH COM PORT 1 OR 2. THIS WILL ALLOW THE HOME CONTROLLER TO CONTROL THE SECURITY SYSTEM AND RECOGNIZE THE STATE OF THE SECURITY SYSTEM AT ALL TIMES. THE HOME CONTROLLER CAN ARM & DISARM THE SECURITY SYSTEM, BYPASS SECURITY ZONES, ACTIVATE THE FIRE, MEDICAL OR POLICE MODES, MONITOR STATUS OF EACH ZONE AND OTHERS. THIS ALLOWS THE HOME CONTROLLER TO ACTIVATE, FOR INSTANCE, THE ARRIVING HOME MODE BY READING WHEN THE FRONT DOOR OR GARAGE DOOR IS OPENED SOME TIME AFTER THE LEAVING HOME MODE WAS ACTIVATED.

- SECURITY PANEL HAS 8 HARDWIRED ZONES EXPANDABLE TO 192. WIRELESS ZONES ARE EXPANABLE TO 48 ZONES. SEE (WWW.CADDX.COM) FOR ADDITION INFO.

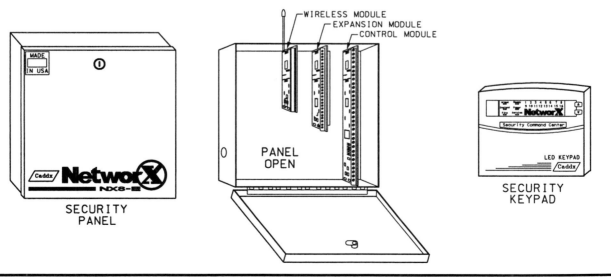

SECURITY PANEL   PANEL OPEN   SECURITY KEYPAD

LEVITON 6417 DHC OR X10 PR511 MOTION DETECTOR FLOODLIGHTS

- TRANSMITS X10 SIGNALS TO ACTIVATE ELCETRICAL DEVICES.
- OFFERS BUILT-IN PHOTOCELL SENSOR THAT CAN TURN ON FOUR X10 CONTROLLED DEVICES AT DUSK AND TURNS THEM BACK OFF AT DAWN.

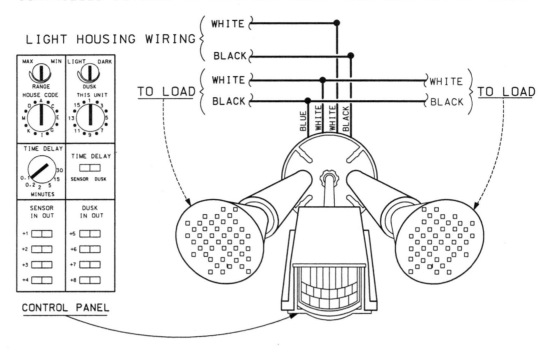

LIGHT HOUSING WIRING

CONTROL PANEL

MINI-TIMER (X10 MT10A) OR (X10 PRO PHT02)

THIS DEVICE IS A PUSH BUTTON TRANSMITTER, ALARM CLOCK AND PROGRAMMABLE SCHEDULER ALL IN ONE.

- ALLOWS USER TO SCHEDULE ON/OFF TIMES FOR UP TO FOUR X10 DEVICES, EACH DEVICE UP TO TWICE A DAY.

- A SECURITY BUTTON AUTOMATICALLY TURNS X10 DEVICES ON AT APPROX- IMATELY THE SCHEDULED TIME TO GIVE HOME A LIVED IN LOOK WHILE OWNER IS AWAY.

- DIM AND BRIGHTEN LIGHTS OR TURN ALL LIGHTS ON OR ALL UNITS OFF USING KEYPAD.

PLUG-IN NOISE FILTER (HOMEPRO AF100) (X10 PRO XPPF)

- LEVITON 6288, 5A 120V 60 Hz RATED. FILTER ELECTRICAL NOISE CREATED BY ELECTRICAL LOADS.

- PLUGS INTO 120V 60Hz RECEPTACLE

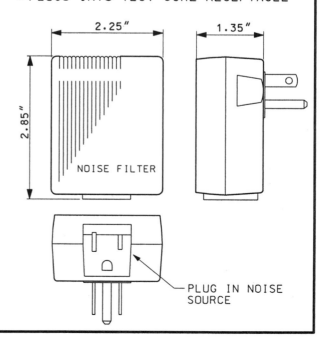

STREET SMART SECURITY WIRELESS KEYCHAIN REMOTE AND RECEIVER

- KEYCHAIN OFFERS 4 BUTTONS AND 6 PROGRAMMABLE OUTPUTS USED TO CONTROL GARAGE DOORS, ACCESS GATE, ETC. OR TO INITIATE HOME AUTOMATION MODES. IS USED TO SECURELY INITIATE THE 'ARRIVING HOME MODE' WHEN INTERFACED WITH A HOME CONTROLLER.

- EACH RECEIVER OUTPUT IS RATED AT 200mA. WHEN USED TO CONTROL 120V TO 480V ELECTRICAL LOADS, A SEPERATE RELAY RATED FOR THE LOAD MUST BE USED.

- THIS DEVICE OFFERS 68 BILLION DIFFERENT CODES THAT ROTATE EACH TIME A TRANSMITTER BUTTON IS PRESSED. THIS ELIMINATES THE POSSIBILITY OF A CRIMINAL FROM CRACKING THE CODES. ALSO OFFERS ANTI-SCAN PROCESSING THAT DOES NOT ALLOW STRAY SIGNALS TO ACTIVATE THE RECEIVER.

- EACH OF 6 OUTPUTS CAN BE PROGRAMMED AS A MOMENTARY OUTPUT, LATCHING OUTPUT OR A TIMED OUTPUT.

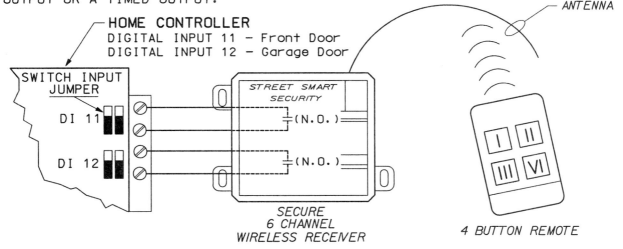

WATERCOP WATER LEAK DETECTION AND DAMAGE PREVENTION SYSTEM

- THE WATERCOP IS A SELF CONTAINED AUTOMATIC WATER SHUTOFF SYSTEM FOR THE HOME OR BUSINESS.

- THE SYSTEM CONSISTS OF TWO PARTS. ONE IS THE WATERCOP RECEIVER AND SHUTOFF VALVE AND THE OTHER IS A WATERHOUND. WATERHOUNDS ARE PLACED IN POTENTIAL LEAK LOCATIONS AND IF THEY DETECT WATER, THEY SEND RF SIGNALS TO THE WATERCOP TO SHUTOFF THE CITY WATER SUPPLY.

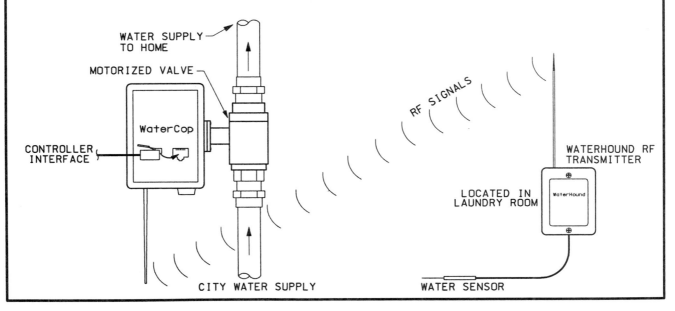

RCS TX15 X10 COMMUNICATING THERMOSTAT

- FEATURES A TWO PART DESIGN. THE MAIN PORTION IS THE TX15 CONTROL UNIT AND THE OTHER COMPONENT IS THE WALL DISPLAY UNIT OR USER INTERFACE.

- FOR STANDARD OR HEAT PUMP HVAC SYSTEMS WITH 2 STAGE HEAT, 1 STAGE COOL. BOTH LOCAL AND REMOTE CONTROL OF ALL THERMOSTAT FUNCTIONS.

- WALL DISPLAY UNIT HAS AN LCD DISPLAY WITH CONTINUOUS BACKLIGHT.

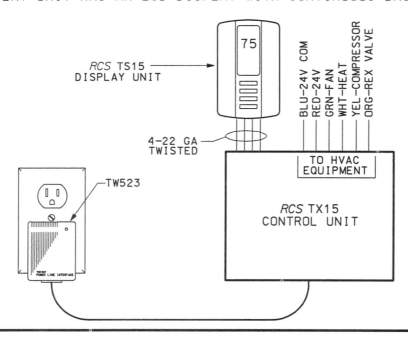

APRILAIRE 8500 SERIES DIGITAL THERMOSTAT

- ONE RELAY CLOSURE FROM AN X10 UNIVERSAL MODULE OR RELAY OUTPUT FROM A HOME CONTROLLER CAN SELECT BETWEEN 2 HEATING OR 2 COOLING TEMPERATURE SET-POINTS.

- SETBACK TEMPERATURE SET-POINT AS PART OF THE FUNCTIONS PERFORMED BY THE 'LEAVING HOME' MODE TO SAVE ENERGY. RESET THE TEMPERATURE SET-POINT AS PART OF THE FUNCTIONS PERFORMED BY THE ARRIVING HOME MODES.

- THE GOOD NIGHT MODE, GOOD MORNING MODE, DAY MODE AND VACATION MODE CAN CHANGE THE TEMPERATURE SET-POINTS AS REQUIRED.

- THERMOSTATS ARE AVAILABLE FOR 1 HEAT, 1 COOL SYSTEMS, HEAT PUMP, 2 HEAT, 1 COOL SYSTEMS AND HEAT PUMP, 2 HEAT, 2 COOL SYSTEMS.

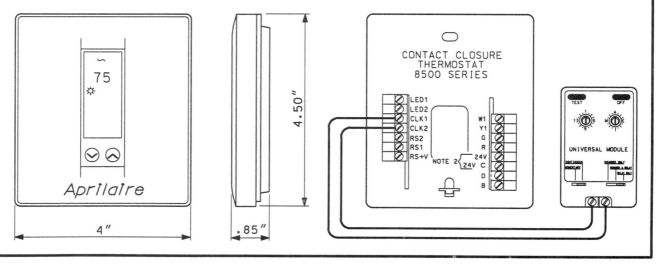

VEHICLE ALERT VEHICLE DETECTOR

- ONE OF TWO AVAILABLE AUXILARY 'FORM' A RELAYS CLOSE IN THE CONSOLE WHEN A VEHICLE IS DETECTED. A RELAY IS CONNECTED TO A DIGITAL INPUT OF A HOME CONTROLLER. THIS NOTIFIES THE HOME CONTROLLER TO ALERT THE OCCUPANTS THROUGH AN AUDIBLE RESPONSE, VOICE RESPONSE OR TO TURN ON LIGHTS, CCTV CAMERAS AND THE TV AND VCR FOR RECORDING PURPOSES. A POWERFLASH MODULE CAN BE USED IN PLACE OF A DIGITAL INPUT AS SHOWN.

- UNIT OFFERS ADJUSTABLE PROBE SENSITIVITY AND A BUILT-IN ALARM.

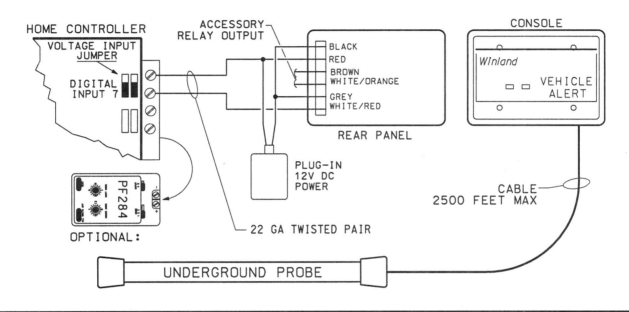

POWER LINE SIGNAL ANALYZER

- POWER LINE SIGNAL ANALYZER PROVIDES FIVE TOOLS TO ANALYZE X10 CONTROL SYSTEMS. THE FIRST TOOL ENABLES THE USER TO MEASURE SIGNAL STRENGTH IN MILLIVOLTS AND IS DISPLAYED ON THE LCD SCREEN.

- THE SECOND TOOL ENABLES THE USER TO MEASURE HIGH LEVELS OF ELECTRICAL NOISE PRESENT ON THE POWER LINES. NOISE IS MEASURED IN MILLIVOLTS AFTER A NUMBER OF MILLISECONDS AFTER THE ZERO DEGREE CROSSING. NOISE ON THE POWER LINES CAN CAUSE INTERFERENCE WITH X10 SIGNALS.

- THE THIRD TOOL ALLOWS THE USER TO IDENTIFY SPECIFIC X10 CODES TRANSMITTED OVER THE POWER LINES. A QUANTITY OF 256 X10 UNIT CODES AND 16 X10 FUNCTION CODES CAN BE DISPLAYED.

- THE FORTH TOOL ENABLES THE USER TO DISSECT X10 SIGNAL TRANSMISSIONS AND THE FIFTH TOOL PROVIDES A RECORD OF THE HISTORY OF X10 TRANSMISSIONS PLACED ON THE POWER LINES.

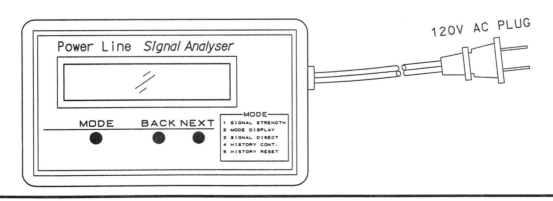

SOMFY DRAPERY MOTOR

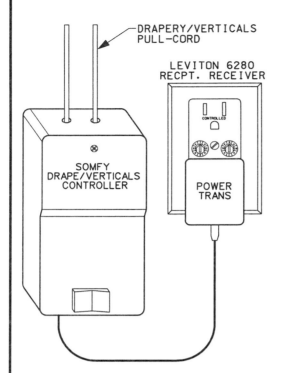

DRAPERY/VERTICALS PULL-CORD

LEVITON 6280 RECPT. RECEIVER

CONTROLLED

POWER TRANS

SOMFY DRAPE/VERTICALS CONTROLLER

- DRAPES ARE AUTOMATED BY INSTALLING A RECEIVER RECEPTACLE OR BY USING A PLUG-IN APPLIANCE MODULE.

- TO OPEN THE DRAPES, TRANSMIT AN X10 OFF COMMAND FOLLOWED BY AN ON COMMAND. AN X10 OFF COMMAND SENT WHILE THE DRAPES ARE IN MOTION WILL STOP THE DRAPES IN MID STREAM. TO CONTINUE OPENING THE DRAPES ANOTHER X10 ON COMMAND IS SENT. WHEN THE DRAPES REACH THE OPEN POSITION, THE INTERNAL LIMIT SWITCHES STOP THE MOTOR.

- TO CLOSE THE DRAPES, TRANSMIT AN X10 OFF COMMAND FOLLOWED BY AN ON COMMAND. AN X10 OFF COMMAND SENT WHILE THE DRAPES ARE IN MOTION WILL STOP THE DRAPES IN MID STREAM. TO CONTINUE CLOSING THE DRAPES ANOTHER X10 ON COMMAND IS SENT. WHEN THE DRAPES REACH THE CLOSED POSITION, THE INTERNAL LIMIT SWITCHES STOP THE MOTOR.

- SOMFY HAS A MANUAL ON/OFF SWITCH ON THE FACE OF THE MOTOR.

AUTOMATIC DRAPE CONTROLLER (ADD-A-MOTOR)

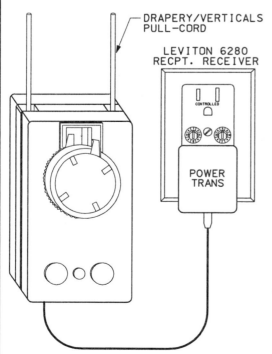

DRAPERY/VERTICALS PULL-CORD

LEVITON 6280 RECPT. RECEIVER

CONTROLLED

POWER TRANS

- DRAPES ARE AUTOMATED BY INSTALLING A RECEIVER RECEPTACLE OR USING A PLUG-IN APPLIANCE MODULE.

- TO OPEN THE DRAPES, TRANSMIT AN X10 OFF COMMAND FOLLOWED BY AN ON COMMAND. AN X10 OFF COMMAND SENT WHILE THE DRAPES ARE IN MOTION WILL STOP THE DRAPES IN MID STREAM. TO CONTINUE OPENING THE DRAPES ANOTHER X10 ON COMMAND IS SENT. WHEN THE DRAPES REACH THE OPEN POSITION, THE INTERNAL LIMIT SWITCHES STOP THE MOTOR.

- TO CLOSE THE DRAPES, TRANSMIT AN X10 OFF COMMAND FOLLOWED BY AN ON COMMAND. AN X10 OFF COMMAND SENT WHILE THE DRAPES ARE IN MOTION WILL STOP THE DRAPES IN MID STREAM. TO CONTINUE CLOSING THE DRAPES ANOTHER X10 ON COMMAND IS SENT. WHEN THE DRAPES REACH THE CLOSED POSITION, THE INTERNAL LIMIT SWITCHES STOP THE MOTOR.

- ADD-A-MOTER HAS A MANUAL ON/OFF SWITCH ON THE FACE OF THE MOTOR.

RECEIVER SWITCH COMPARISON CHART

MODEL NUMBER	MANUFACTURER	MAXIMUM RATING	TRUE ROCKER SWITCH	AGC/NOISE REDUCTION	DIMMING BY X10	DIMMING AT SWITCH	SOFT START & RESUME DIM	3-WAY READY	2-WAY X10 CONTROL	LED INDICATOR	SCENE LIGHTING CAPABLE	LOW VOLTAGE LIGHTING	INCANDESCENT LIGHTING	240V ELECTRICAL LOADS	CEILING FANS	FLUORESCENT LIGHTS	BATHROOM FANS	WATER HEATER 20 AMP MAX	240V 2HP MAX PUMPS	REQUIRES A NEUTRAL WIRE
6383-WI	LEVITON	500W		●	●	●	●	●					●							
6291	LEVITON	15A		●						●		●	●		●	●	●			●
HCM06-1SW	LEVITON	600W	●	●	●	●	●	●		●	●	●	●							●
HCM10-1SW	LEVITON	1000W	●	●	●	●	●	●		●	●	●	●							●
HCM06-1DW	LEVITON	600W	●	●	●	●	●	●		●	●	●	●							●
HCM10-1DW	LEVITON	1000W	●	●	●	●	●	●		●	●	●	●							●
HCM06-1TW	LEVITON	600W	●	●	●	●	●	●	●	●	●	●	●							●
HCS10-1SW	LEVITON	1200W	●	●						●	●	●	●		●	●	●			●
6371	LEVITON	20A		●										●				●	●	
6375	LEVITON	15A								●			●		●	●	●			●
6376	LEVITON	300W			●								●							●
XPD3	X10 PRO	500W			●	●		●					●							
XPS3	X10 PRO	20A							●		●		●		●	●	●			●
XPDF	X10 PRO	300W			●								●							●
XPFM	X10 PRO	15A								●			●		●	●	●			
RD101	HOMEPRO	500W			●	●		●					●							
RS100	HOMEPRO	20A							●		●	●	●		●	●	●			●
RS210	HOMEPRO	20A												●				●	●	
SS1L/S600	PCS	600W	●		●	●	●	●		●	●	●	●		●	●	●			●
SS1L/S1000	PCS	1000W	●		●	●	●	●		●	●	●	●		●	●	●			●
2384	SWITCHLINC	600W	●	●	●	●	●	●		●		●	●		●		●			●
2385	SWITCHLINC	600W	●	●				●		●		●	●		●	●	●			●
2386	SWITCHLINC	600W	●		●	●	●	●		●		●	●		●		●			●
2380	SWITCHLINC	600W	●		●	●	●	●		●		●	●		●		●			●
2381	SWITCHLINC	1000W	●	●	●	●	●	●	●	●	●	●	●		●		●			●
MS12A	X10	500W			●	●							●							
CI1600VA	COMPOSE	600W	●		●	●	●	●		●	●		●							
CI11000VA	COMPOSE	1000W	●		●	●	●	●		●	●		●							
CI11000ND	COMPOSE	1000VA	●					●	●	●	●	●	●		●	●	●			●

Popular Home Automation Websites

- Smarthome.com – www.smarthome.com
- Home Controls, Inc. – www.homecontrols.com
- EH Publishing, Inc. – www.electronichouse.com
- HomeTech Solutions – www.hometechsolutions.com
- Smart Home Systems USA – www.smarthomeusa.com
- Worthington Distribution – www.worthdist.com
- JDS Technologies – www.jdstechnologies.com
- Electronic House Magazine – www.electronichouse.com
- Home Automation Association – www.homeautomation.org
- Leviton – www.leviton.com
- Advanced Control Technologies, Inc. (ACT) – www.act-solutions.com
- SwitchLinc – www.smarthome.com
- HomePro – www.smarthomepro.com
- X-10 Pro – www.x10pro.com
- X-10 (USA), Inc. – www.x10.com
- Residential Control Systems (*RCS*) – www.resconsys.com
- Home Automation, Inc. – www.homeauto.com
- Digital Security Controls (DSC) – www.dsc.com
- Xantech – www.xantech.com
- Winland Electronics, Inc. – www.winland.com
- Street Smart Security – www.streetsmartsecurity.com
- Home Director – www.homedirector.com
- Aprilaire – www.aprilaire.com
- Compose PLC – www.composeplc.com
- Powerline Control Systems (PCS) – www.pcslighting.com
- Caddx Security Systems – www.caddx.com
- Elk Products, Inc. – www.elkproducts.com
- ADI – www.adilink.com
- Aqualine – www.aqualine.com
- asiHome – www.asihome.net
- Home Automator Magazine – www.homeautomator.com
- Home Toys – www.hometoys.com
- *i*Automate – www.iautomate.com
- Somfy – www.somfy.com
- Automation and Security Technology – www.homeautomationnet.com
- FutureSmart – www.futuresmart.com
- Broadband Utopia – www.broadbandutopia.com

Glossary of Terms

AC (alternating current) – The available current from electrical power systems in USA homes. An electric current that reverses its direction sixty times per second or 60 Hz.

Address – The combination of a Letter code and a Number code assigned to and set on each RECEIVER switch.

A/D – Analog to Digital converts analog voltages into a digital representation compatible with the Stargate or CommStar.

AMPERE – A unit of electrical current equal to one volt across one ohm of resistance. Abbreviated as amp or A.

ANALOG INPUT – A linear voltage from 0-5V DC received by the I/O of the Home Controller and used in the IF statement of an Event. **IF** 75 degrees F, **THEN** turn ON pump.

ASCII – ASCII (American Standard Code for Information Interchange): The universal standard for representing text letters, numerals, punctuation marks and control instructions in computer storage and communication.

A/V – Audio and video equipment

CAT 5 – Short for Category 5 Unshielded Twisted Pair. A standard for copper wiring designed specifically for electronic data.

CATV – A broadband communications technology in which multiple television channels as well as audio and data signals may be transmitted either one way or bi-directionally through an often hybrid (fiber and coaxial) distribution system to a single or to multiple specific locations.

CO2 – Carbon Dioxide

CCTV – Closed circuit TV

CIRCUIT – The complete cyclic path of an electric current that includes the source of electric energy.

COMMANDS – Messages that a controller (i.e: Home Controller, X10 Transmitter, IR Controller, Telephone Controller, etc.) sends to an actuating device that ultimately changes the state of an electrical load or mechanical device.

CONDUCTOR – Refers to an electrical wire that provides a path for current to flow.

CONTACTS – Electrical conductive points, or sets of points that open and close electrical circuits that ultimately control electrical loads.

CONTROLLER – Can be a Home Controller, IR-Xpander, TeleCommand, Telemaster phone controller or other IR, RF or X10 Transmitter.

CURRENT – The flow of electrons through a conductor. Units of current is amps.

CYCLE – 1 revolution of a 60 Hz sine wave from zero degrees back to zero degrees.

DC – Direct current – An electrical current flowing in one direction only and constant in value.

DIGITAL INPUT (DI) – Closing of a circuit that produces a voltage differential of 4-24V DC across a set of Digital Input terminals of the Home Controller I/O, which is used by the Home Controller to base control decisions on.

DIRECT TRANSMISSION – Refers to X10 signals that are sent from a Transmitter directly to the Receiver switch to control an electrical device without help from a Home Controller.

DP – Refers to double pole contacts. Includes a (N.O.) and (N.C.) contacts as part of a relay.

DRY CONTACT – Metal points that close to complete a circuit or open to break a circuit.

ELECTRICAL NOISE – Random high frequency electrical signals that travel over the power lines produced by electrical loads or by the electrical power system.

EXIT DELAY – This allows a person to ARM the security system and leave through a protected entrance without causing an alarm.

EVENT – An Event ultimately controls one or more electrical loads in sequence. An Event consists of programming lines used by the Home Controller that contains an **IF** statement and a **THEN** statement. The **IF** statement must become true before the **THEN** statement sends out control commands to control electrical loads.

GA – Refers to the word gauge, which is used to identify the size of a conductor.

GANG – Refers to a space within an electrical enclosure to install a 120V X10 Receiver switch, Receiver receptacle or Transmitter.

GND – Refers to a home's ground wire(s) or grounding rod.

GFI – Ground fault interrupter is a type of power receptacle that is used to break the circuit to protect individuals from electrical shock.

HARDWIRED – Refers to the use of hard conductors or wiring connected from Analog and Digital Input sources to the I/O, and from an I/O Relay Output to a controlled device.

HVAC – Heating, Ventilating, and air conditioning system. A mechanical system that provides heating, cooling and fresh air ventilation for the home.

HOME RUN WIRING – A wiring method that connects each sensor or contacts directly to the control panel instead of wiring two sensors or more in series away from the panel.

HOME CONTROLLER – A device that has decision making capabilities. A device that can receive X10 commands, Analog and Digital Inputs, IR commands, ASCII and RS-232/485 communications used to initiate Events. Events contain sequences of commands initiated by the Home Controller to control electrical loads. The Home Controller controls these loads through X10 commands, hardwired Relay Outputs, IR commands, ASCII communications, RS-232/485 communications.

I/O – Input/Output communications in reference to Analog & Digital Inputs or Relay Outputs.

HERTZ – The number of cycles per second of an electromagnetic wave; one Hz is equal to one cycle per second. The name comes from Heinrich R. Hertz, the German physicist who discovered electromagnetic waves.

INDIRECT TRANSMISSION – Refers to X10 signals sent from a Transmitter to the Home Controller to initiate a Mode/Event. This Mode will control one or more Receiver switches that are set to different codes than what the Transmitter is set to.

IR – Infrared signals used to control electrical equipment.

kHz – 1 kHz = 1000 hertz. Hertz is a unit of frequency equal to one cycle per second.

KILOWATT (kW) – 1 kW = 1000 watts. A unit of power. (Amps x Volts) = Watts

kOhm – Kilo-ohm = 1000 ohms, A unit of electrical resistance.

LCD – A digital display that uses liquid crystal cells that change reflectivity in an applied electric field; used for portable computer keypad displays.

LED – A type of diode that emits light when current passes through it. Depending on the material used, the color can be visible or infrared.

LETTER CODE – A letter code can be letters A thru P. They are the first digit of a Receiver address or Transmitter code setting.

LINE – The hot or live wire that supplies AC power to an electrical load.

LOAD – An electrical device or the amount of power (Watts) required by an electrical device to operate properly.

LOW VOLTAGE – Low voltage in this publication is considered to be between 6V – 28V DC or AC.

MACRO – A Macro consists of a series of control commands sent from a Controller. The Controller's Event **THEN** statement contains this series of control commands.

MAGNETIC CONTACT – A sensory component used to detect movable objects such as windows & doors for security purposes and to initiate modes. It consists of two separate parts, a magnetically activated switch and a magnet. Moving the magnet causes the switch mechanism to open and close.

mA – One thousandth of an ampere

mV – Is equal to 1000th of a volt

MODE – See the description of an Event.

MODULE – A Receiver switch that simply plugs into a power receptacle while the electrical load it controls plugs into the Module.

NEUTRAL WIRE – A grounded conductor that completes a circuit by providing a path back to the power source. Generally identified by a white insulator over a 120V AC conductor.

N.C. – NORMALLY CLOSED – A circuit or switch in which the contacts are **closed** when the device is de-energized.

N.O. – NORMALLY OPEN – A circuit or switch in which the contacts are **opened** when the device is de-energized.

NUMBER CODE – A number code can be any number from 1 to 16. Number codes are the second portion of a Receiver address or transmission code.

PC – Personal Computer

PPM Parts Per Million – Used to specify the concentration (by volume) of a gas or vapor at low concentration, or a dissolved material at high dilution.

PLC – Power-line Carrier: A home automation system protocol that provides the transmission of digital X10 signals over the power lines in the home for purposes of communicating to Receiver in the system that ultimately respond to control electrical loads.

PROTOCOL – A specific type of home automation form of communication and technology.

PROVERTER – A device that converts RS-485 to RS-232 communication.

RADIO FREQUENCY (RF) – An electro-magnetic wave frequency located between infrared frequencies and audio frequencies used for the purpose of providing radio transmissions.

RECEIVER – A Power-line Carrier device that receives X10 signals from a Transmitting device, which is usually set to the same address to provide remote control of an electrical load.

RELAY – An electromagnetic device used for remote control purposes. This device is actuated by power in an electric circuit to operate other devices in a different circuit.

RELAY OUTPUT (RO) – (N.O.) or (N.C.), 1 amp @ 24 VDC rated contacts on the I/O used to close or open a circuit for the purpose of controlling an electrical load.

RESISTANCE – A property of a conductor opposing the passage of electric current.

RESUME DIM – A control function available on some X10 technology Receiver switches. Each time these types of Receivers are turned ON they will brighten to the dim level that they were previously at before they were turned OFF.

RG-6 – A 75 ohm coaxial cable which will handle CATV, satellite, high definition TV and cable modems with additional shielding to prevent noise. RG-6 is also the current recommendation for CATV residential applications.

RS-232 – Recommended Standard-232. An Electronics Industries Association standard asynchronous serial line, which is used commonly for modems, computer terminals, and serial printers. RS-232 uses a 25-pin or 9-pin connector. The standard designates the purpose for each of the 25 or 9 lines, including lines for sending and receiving data, ground connections, and control lines.

R-VALUE – A unit of thermal resistance used for comparing insulating values of different material. The higher the R-value of a material, the greater its insulating properties are, which slows down the flow of heat through the material.

SET-BACK TEMPERATURE – A temperature set-point selected for the cooling mode, which is higher than the design set-point for energy conservation purposes. In the heating mode the set-point temperature will be lower than the heating design set-point for the purpose of saving energy.

SIGNAL COLLISION – This condition is caused by two or more X10 transmissions on the power lines at the same time, which essentially cancels one or both transmissions.

SLAVE – A mechanism under control of the actions of a similar mechanism. Normally used with a PLC 3-way Receiver switch or Relay device.

SOFT-START – A control function available on some X10 technology Receiver switches. Each time these type of Receivers are turn ON they will brighten upward from an OFF state to the previous brightness level. When an OFF command is performed they will slowly dim down until the light it completely OFF.

SOLENOID VALVE – A valve that is actuated by applying electrical current to a coil that opens or closes the valve. N.O. and N.C. Solenoid valves are available.

SUB-PANEL – A secondary power distribution panel that furnishes a smaller amount of power to electrical circuits in comparison to what the main distribution panel provides.

THERMOSTAT – An automatic control device designed to be responsive to changes in temperature. This device is used to maintain a set-point temperature by controlling the appropriate HVAC mechanical equipment.

TRANSMITTER – A Power-line Carrier device that sends X10 signals over the power lines for the intended Receiver(s) to accept and respond to.

VOLT – Electromotive force equal to the difference of the potential between two points. Abbreviation for volt is V.

VA – Volts times amperes; an electrical measurement. For direct current, one volt-amp equals the same power as one watt.

WATT – (W) A unit of measure of electric power at a point in time, as capacity or demand. A watt equals 1 Joule of energy per second.

ZONES – A region or area set off as distinct from surrounding areas.

ZERO DEGREE CROSSING – The midpoint of the amplitude of an AC sine wave, which is where X10 signals travel.

Structured Wiring Design Manual

By: Robert N. Bucceri

Easy to read and follow!

- SECOND EDITION -

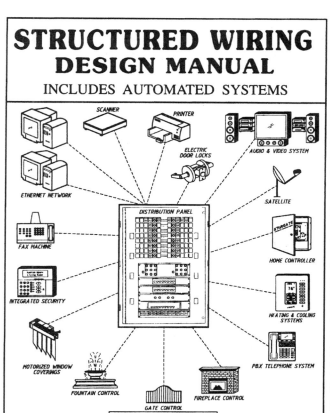

Learn how to design and install *Structured Wiring Systems* with the latest in product technology.

This book centers around an 'Example Home' that consists of a highly detailed *Structured Wiring Systems* that illustrates each and every cable and wire termination that makes up the entire system. Over 150 detailed floor plans, wiring schematics and illustrations with an explanation of each.

This book goes well beyond a tutorial of a typical *Structured Wiring System* by featuring PBX Digital Telephone Systems, Broadband Ethernet Networks, Whole House Audio & Video Systems, Lighting Control Systems, Integrated Security Systems, CCTV Camera Surveillance, Heating & Cooling Systems, Motorized Systems, Water Systems, as well as other systems that are controlled by the *Stargate* Interactive Home Controller.

Provides a 'Step-By-Step' approach to learning the following:

- How to layout the system based on the customer's requirements
- How to design, layout and position the Equipment Room in a home
- What type of cable and other system components to use for each subsystem
- How to perform the rough-in process
- How to pull 'Service Input Cables' and 'Drop Cables' through all portions of the home
- How to perform the trim-out process
- How to perform cable terminations
- How to test cables after the system is installed
- How to program automated systems
- What to do and what not to do during the design and installation process

A must-have manual for the 'do-it-yourselfer' and the 'installing dealer' alike!

LATEST TECHNOLOGY IN AUTOMATED HOME CONTROL

SYSTEM DESIGN MANUAL USING X-10 & HARDWIRED PROTOCOLS

By: Robert Bucceri

A Practical Approach to Designing Your Home Automation System

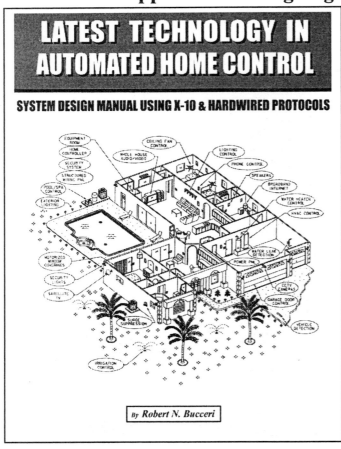

Includes the Following Subjects:

- X-10 Power-Line Carrier Systems
- Hardwired I/O Based Systems
- Automated X-10 Lighting Systems
- Automated Appliance
- Automated Single-Zone HVAC Systems
- Automated Multi-Zone HVAC Systems
- X-10 RS-232 and RS-485 HVAC Control
- Automated Multi-Zone Sprinkler Systems
- Automated Multi-Zone Audio/Video Systems
- Automated CCTV Camera Surveillance System
- Automated Pool and Spa Systems
- Integrated Security Systems
- Automated Security Lighting
- Energy & Water Management Systems
- Automated Access Gate & Garage Door Control
- Automated Window Covering Control
- Automated Water Heater Control
- Automated Water Leak Detection System
- Automated Vehicle Detection Systems
- Automated Ceiling Fans
- Automated Attic Fan Systems
- RF Control Systems
- Surge Suppressor Systems
- Electrical Noise Suppression Systems

Also Includes:
- Examining the Home Prior to Designing the Home Automation System
- Measuring Signal Strength and Finding Electrical Noise Sources
- Room By Room Design Process
- X-10 Trouble Shooting Principles
- X-10 Signal Coupling and Amplification Methods
- X-10 Signal Blocking Methods
- Home Automation System Controller Programming
- 26 Modes of Operation

ISBN 0-9700057-2-5   Copyright 2003

NOTES:

NOTES:

NOTES:

NOTES: